Praise for *America Needs America's Energy*

"Through his many years of experience, Mark Stansberry successfully challenges us toward developing a comprehensive American energy plan."

—Bill Anoatubby
Governor, the Chickasaw Nation

"As Mark states, 'The time has come for all of us, the people, to take control of our energy future here in America.' He and I have discussed the importance of moving inevitably toward a hydrogen economy. I believe, after reviewing all the energy options presented in his book, it should move us closer to achieving that possibility. The *future* is now for us and our children. We cannot wait any longer.

"*America Needs America's Energy* provides more in-depth insight from Mark Stansberry into the significance of energy to America. Today, the book is significant for two reasons. For one, the perspective of the book is not political or even economical. It focuses on the need for people and communities rather than governments and corporations. Energy involves and impacts everything we do every day with its role in our daily lives, work, vacation, and health. As the subtitle puts it: 'creating together the People's Energy Plan.'

"The other reason is the need for a People's Energy Plan not only for our everyday lives, but also for our public policy makers and industry. Every family has a plan—for their lifestyle, children, college, homes, investments, future, and retirement. The fact, as the book points out, that there has *never* been an energy plan for America is a serious concern for every American. If we, as a nation, are to survive, we need a plan for making our nation energy independent, using our natural resources such as natural gas but primarily wind, sun, and water. If not, we will continue to be caught in conflicts and wars for generations to come."

—Woodrow W. Clark II, MA[3], PhD
Qualitative economist, Clark Strategic Partners
Corecipient of the Nobel Peace Prize

"America's energy policy cannot simply be cheap energy. Mark Stansberry tells us how to break out and assume an energy-secure and dynamic future economy."

—Frank Keating
Governor of Oklahoma, 1995–2003
President, American Bankers Association

"More than ever energy is a key strategic issue for America. Mark Stansberry knows the subject well, and he is an experienced person in national public policy and its implementation. This book clarifies ways forward and is an excellent guide for citizens and policy-makers alike."

—Michael Warder
Vice chancellor, Pepperdine University

"Now is the time to act, and this book moves us toward action."

—Ambassador James Jones
Former Congressman, chairman of the American Stock Exchange, and US ambassador to Mexico

"Mark Stansberry has illuminated the energy issues from all sides, which not only increases the reader's awareness and education, but provides a necessary call to action as to what one individual can do to make energy more available, environmentally friendly, and affordable."

—Dennis McCuistion
Executive director, Institute for Excellence in Corporate Governance, University of Texas at Dallas

"A national energy policy—what a concept! Mark Stansberry gets it! His book ought to be mandatory reading for all congressional candidates and every constituent before they run for office or vote. Mark is a brilliant energy thought leader and an articulate author whose ideas are timely and important for our nation's global competitiveness."

—Richard P. Rush
Chairman, Rush Strategies

"*America Needs America's Energy* challenges us to achieve energy independence. This book should be at the forefront of debate when it comes to our energy future."

—Jose Beceiro
Director of clean energy and economic development,
Austin Chamber of Commerce

"Mark Stansberry's book *America Needs America's Energy* is a must-read, a necessary formula for our very survival. And we have no time to waste!"

—William S. Banowsky
Former president, Gaylord Broadcasting

"*America Needs America's Energy* should be read by all concerned citizens and office holders."

—Michael C. Carnuccio
President, Oklahoma Council of Public Affairs, Inc.

"America needs American energy if we are going to continue providing food for America's tables at the most affordable cost found anywhere in the world. We must continue to research all types and forms of energy to assure energy independence for future generations."

—Terry Detrick
President, American Farmers and Ranchers
Third generation farmer and rancher

AMERICA
Needs America's
ENERGY

For Kelly —

AMERICA
Needs America's
ENERGY

Creating Together the People's Energy Plan !

Mark A. Stansberry (signature)

Mark A. Stansberry

Brown Books Publishing Group
Dallas, Texas

America Needs America's Energy
Creating Together the People's Energy Plan

Brown Books Publishing Group
16250 Knoll Trail, Suite 205
Dallas, Texas 75248
www.BrownBooks.com
(972) 381-0009

ISBN 978-1-61254-071-9
Library of Congress Control Number 2012938835

Printed in the United States of America
10 9 8 7 6 5 4 3 2 1

For more information, please visit: www.PeoplesEnergyPlan.com
or www.EnergyAdvocates.org.

For:

Sherman E. Smith and family, Will Smith, and Beverly Marquardt

The founders, past and present members, board members, officers, and sponsors of The Energy Advocates

Those who have sacrificed and dedicated their lives to the energy industry

The supporting families of American energy industry workers

My wife, Nancy; our children, Joe, Matt, and Aubrey, and their spouses; and our grandchildren

My parents, George and Lucy Stansberry

My sister, Mary Fern Carpenter

Above all else, thanks to God for providing us with the natural resources to provide energy!

The Energy Prayer

A decade ago, Nancy Huff of Broken Arrow, Oklahoma, met then-Secretary of State Colin Powell at the National Prayer Breakfast. During their meeting, Secretary Powell asked Nancy to pray for Oklahoma to produce more oil because he believed our country needed that oil. When Nancy returned to Oklahoma from Washington, DC, she became active in The Energy Advocates and wrote a special book of prayers for the oil and gas industry. She prayed with a group every Thursday night for Oklahoma, the US, and the industry. I share with you one of those energy prayers:

> Father, I come to you and I ask protection for every drilling site, pipeline, refinery, production site, oil truck, tanker, or any other means of obtaining and transporting oil in the United States.
>
> Protect all those who work in the oil industry, and give them safety and wisdom about every potentially dangerous situation.
>
> I ask, as the oil and gas industry in this country grows, that the environment would be protected.
>
> I ask for the development of new technology that will enable those in the energy industry to drill efficiently while protecting the environment.
>
> Thank you for your hand of safety on the industry and the land that has helped to make the country great.
>
> Amen.

Contents

Foreword

When I was elected president of the University of Oklahoma in 1978, one of my earliest office appointments was with two of Oklahoma's oil and gas geniuses: Lew O. Ward from Enid and Robert A. Hefner III from Oklahoma City.

Here was their urgent message: "Bill, we appreciate your broad academic mandate, but there is something that you must know. Energy is the future of Oklahoma! OU needs to establish an Energy Center." So we created Sarkeys Energy Center, a groundbreaking scientific academic complex that today houses the largest geophysical reference library in the world. Lew and Bob also observed, "We must always keep drilling for oil. But we must especially remember, and strongly emphasize, that the ultimate future for Oklahoma and America will depend upon natural gas. God blessed Oklahoma with enough natural gas for centuries to come. It is clean and enormously plentiful. But it is also very deep and we must often depend upon expensive and even experimental mechanical solutions. President Banowsky," they pleaded, "please do everything you possibly can at OU, and everywhere else, to encourage and increase the flow of natural gas."

Bob Hefner and Lew Ward are, of course, still going strong as national leaders of this crucial campaign. But now they have been reinforced by a dynamic Oklahoma leader. Mark A. Stansberry has emerged with the same Hefner-Ward intelligence, vision, courage, imagination, and absolute determination.

Mark A. Stansberry knows who he is and where he is. He now lives in Edmond, but his deep Oklahoma roots run all the way out to his Elk City hometown. Mark is a strong Christian who has traveled and worked in many countries throughout the world. He is a distinguished international businessman and humanitarian. But he is preeminently a global energy leader. He is the founder and chairman of the GTD Group; host of the radio show *The Weekly Roundtable*, broadcast weekly from Tulsa; chairman of People to People International; and, of great interest to us, he authored the powerful, groundbreaking book *The Braking Point: America's Energy Dreams and Global Economic Realities*. In his book, Mark stated, "Failure to effectively deal with this problem now will threaten our nation's economic prosperity and compromise our national security, and could radically alter our way of life . . . hence, the braking point!"

Mark and I are lifelong friends. How thrilled I am that he now comes out of his vast experience with this latest groundbreaking book. It gives every promise of being even more powerful than the first. Hopefully, it will be the perfect companion for Robert A. Hefner III's book, *The Grand Energy Transition* (or *The GET*).

Mark Stansberry's book *America Needs America's Energy* is a must-read, a necessary formula for our very survival. And we have no time to waste! We have already entered political, cultural, and class warfare that leaves millions of Americans utterly in the dark. Can you imagine the president of the United States, Barak Obama, completely canceling in a highly arbitrary manner the entire Keystone XL pipeline project?

The international greatness of the University of Oklahoma testifies, in part, to the power and efficacy of the energy industry. My earlier presidency at Pepperdine University further makes the case. When I became president in the 1960s, Pepperdine College was dying on thirty acres with eight hundred students in the Los Angeles ghetto. Today's Pepperdine University was created by the Hydril Oil Company. They gave us $300 million and sent us out near the ocean on an eight-hundred-acre Malibu campus that today has eight thousand students.

Mark serves on the board for his alma mater, Oklahoma Christian University; the Academy of Leadership and Liberty; the UCO Foundation; The Fund for American Studies (TFAS); the Oklahoma Heritage Association–Gaylord-Pickens Museum, while also serving as corporate secretary; and he has in the past served on the Board of Visitors of Pepperdine University's School of Public Policy, along with other boards and advisory committees. In recognition of his countless contributions, in 2009 Mark was inducted into the Western Oklahoma Hall of Fame.

With more than thirty years of direct experience in the Oklahoma energy industry, Mark Stansberry has become a respected industry expert and media commentator on energy issues. He has been invited to testify before the US Senate Energy and Natural Resources Committee; served an eight-year term as chairman of the State Chamber of Oklahoma Energy Council; and founded and chairs the International Energy Policy Conference, now in its twentieth year.

On top of all this, Mark and Nancy Stansberry have three grown children and six grandchildren, an energy industry all of their own.

—William Slater Banowsky

President emeritus, Pepperdine University
President emeritus, University of Oklahoma
Former president of Gaylord Broadcasting

Acknowledgments

This book is made possible through the support of The Energy Advocates and the great assistance of Joe Stansberry, Nancy Stansberry, Ben Bennett, and 29E Inc., who helped me research and review the materials used in this book. Many thanks are also due to Milli Brown, owner of Brown Books Publishing Group, for her advice and counsel; Auburn Layman, editorial coordinator; Nan Bauroth, editor; Cindy Birne and Cathy Williams, PR and marketing; Haley Doran, project coordinator; Jessica Burnham, production manager; and Omar Mediano, cover designer—all of whom helped shepherd the book through the publication process.

It is not the critic who counts; not the man who points out how the strong man stumbles, or where the doer of deeds could have done better. The credit belongs to the man who is actually in the arena, whose face is marred by dust and sweat and blood; who strives valiantly; who errs and comes up short again and again, because there is no effort without error or shortcoming; but who knows the great enthusiasms, the great devotions; who spends himself for a worthy cause; who, at the best, knows, in the end, the triumph of high achievement, and who, at the worst, if he fails, at least he fails while daring greatly, so that his place shall never be with those cold and timid souls who knew neither victory nor defeat.

—Theodore Roosevelt

Introduction

In 2008 when I published *The Braking Point: America's Energy Dreams and Global Economic Realities*, I expressed my view that America and the world were facing an energy crisis. The good news was that America's energy problems could be solved. The bad news was that our country's energy crisis did not exist in a vacuum, was not temporary, and would not fix itself. At that time I stressed that failure to effectively deal with this problem would threaten our nation's economic prosperity and compromise our national security, and could radically alter our way of life. The book's title, *The Braking Point*, said it all: America needed to put on the brakes, stop, and assess the entire energy picture to see where our country was headed.

Five years later, the United States still does not have a strategic energy plan. From President Nixon in 1970 up to President Obama in 2012, we have been told time and again that an energy policy is in the works and a national energy plan is on the way. However, this lack of urgency comes as no surprise to me. For the first thirty years of my career in the energy industry, very little serious attention was paid by the media or government officials to energy policy and issues. That complacency finally began to change about the same time that I wrote *The Braking Point* as politicians sensed that energy security had emerged as a critical issue.

In 2008 former Speaker of the House Newt Gingrich broke ground in his book, *Drill Here, Drill Now, Pay Less*, noting, "America is suffering from an artificial energy crisis that is also a dangerous national security crisis—artificial, because America is gifted with enormous reserves of energy."[1] In 2011 President Clinton took up the topic in *Back to Work*, insisting, "The surest way to create jobs, cut costs, enhance national security, cut the trade deficit by up to 50 percent, and fight global warming is to change the way we produce and consume energy."[2] Most recently, former Arkansas Governor Mike Huckabee addressed security aspects of energy policy in *A Simple Government*, cautioning, "Let's not forget about the national security threats that we face every day because of our dependence on foreign oil. Countries like Saudi Arabia that make billions from us like to showcase glittering new public works projects and the like. But behind the walls they are also funding the very schools, or madrassas, that recruit, radicalize, and then train impressionable children for what is essentially the Future Terrorists of the World Club."[3]

As the national debate over energy policy escalates, the tendency is to point fingers at companies in the energy business or a lack of will among elected officials to come to grips with the situation. It's been them vs. us, with "them" not always clearly defined. I contend, however, that for too long we have been wasting time blaming the energy industry or the government for failure to adopt a national energy strategy when we, the people, should be responsible for creating the plan. As consumers of energy, we should drive the process, evaluating how we can best leverage our natural resources here at home to assure long-term energy independence and security.

Devising such a plan begins with the recognition that the United States has not independently advanced itself from the Industrial Revolution to the Information Age to become reliant on foreign oil—let alone from known enemies. Not a one of us would think to ask for a cup of sugar from a neighbor who is hostile or whom we fear. Yet America is now paying for its energy resources from nations we do not trust, and in some cases, nations that openly advocate our downfall.

Our national security has long been one of the most important assets we cherish. For that reason we cannot afford to become addicted to energy at any cost. Today, nothing in America moves without energy, but the definition of energy security also extends to power generation. To be independent means not just avoiding foreign oil, but creating a forward-thinking infrastructure that provides for our lifestyle needs. Whenever we flip a light switch in this country, the lights turn on. Many people overseas do not enjoy that certainty. For instance, while visiting the Czech Republic not long ago, I rode in an elevator that would stop and then start again due to intermittent energy. Americans would never tolerate that kind of situation. We take our energy security for granted—an attitude that ultimately could prove dangerous for our economic and national security well-being.

Second, we have to accept that a viable energy plan requires the private and public sector to work together. Since I entered the energy business in 1977, the industry has continually been forced to defend itself. For example, in 1985 I testified before the US Senate and Natural Resources Committee in a forty-three-page report on the potentially devastating effects that proposed regulations would have on the oil and gas industry in Oklahoma, in terms of job loss and reductions in drilling expenditures, at a time when this vital industry most needed support. American oil and gas companies have a history of being major contributors to their communities by providing funds for local schools, hospitals, and charities. To achieve energy independence, the American people must rally behind these companies and recognize the essential role they play in powering our lives 24–7 at home and work.

Third, as the title of this book advocates, America needs America's energy. This is not just a concept, but a truth. In the four years since *The Braking Point* was published, several significant advances in the energy business hold promise of helping us establish energy independence. For starters, there has been a dramatic increase in natural gas supplies in our nation due to shale gas drilling that uses a technology known as hydraulic fracturing. As Chart 1 illustrates, the lower forty-eight states contain a potential wealth of shale plays.

Chart 1

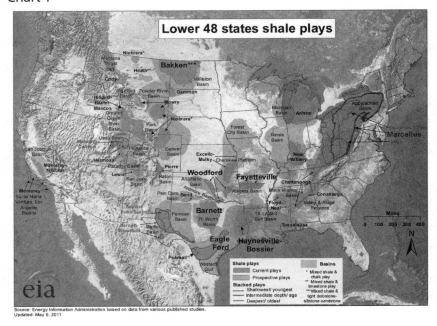

Simultaneously, we are enjoying a tremendous increase in our oil reserves due to activity in drilling, primarily in the Bakken play in North Dakota and Montana.

Chart 1a

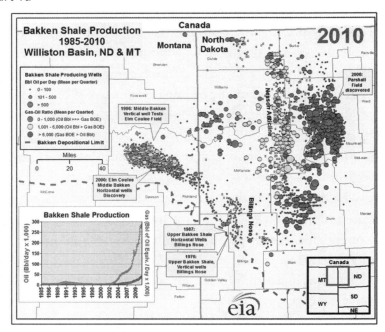

As Chart 1a shows, this activity is not only helping offset a decline in oil production from the long-established oil field in Prudhoe Bay, Alaska, but also driving a boom in jobs and newfound prosperity for communities in these two states.

Despite these positive signs, the need for an energy plan is more urgent than ever. Why? Because it takes so many years to build an effective, efficient infrastructure. The best analogy is our interstate highway system. If not for the vision of President Eisenhower back in the 1950s to construct this massive infrastructure, the road system we so heavily rely on today wouldn't exist. Contrast that with the 1978 Fuels Act under President Carter, who insisted we didn't have enough natural gas, so we needed to go back to coal. Such unwillingness to confront the problem set us back years, the consequences of which we are still suffering today. That is why we can no longer wait. We must develop a strategic energy plan for the future or we will reach the point where we regress to the status of third-world countries with brownouts, or even worse, blackmail and subjection to price control by enemy states. America cannot and should not ever find itself in the position of having to ration power simply because we don't have the willingness to plan.

The good news is that some people here aren't waiting for a mandate. As I travel the country educating people about the need for America to deploy its own energy resources, I've discovered cities are already looking at different approaches. For instance, Austin, Texas is testing a smart grid, a biomass plant is operating in Wichita, Kansas, and up in North Dakota the emphasis is on oil. Other cities in Texas are looking at wind power, while Oklahoma is focusing on natural gas. A national plan doesn't mean we all rely on natural gas, or wind, or solar power, but that we tailor our approach based on the resources indigenous to our area, along with expanding into other energy sources that are easily transported. Even though energy in Oklahoma is centered on natural gas, we have an abundance of natural gas nationwide that will enable us to build an infrastructure clear across the country that everyone can tap.

These examples are but a few of the signs on the horizon that the issue of energy security is at last reaching critical mass. This book is dedicated to the proposition that we need an energy revolution in this country right now, and the leaders should be we, the people. By turning to new technologies, innovation, and the enduring American spirit that has enabled us to overcome every challenge this nation has faced since our founding, the goal of total energy independence can be achieved before it is too late. And we are the ones who will have to do it, because our societal institutions have proven they are not up to the task.

With that as inspiration, I invite you to join me in part 1 as we explore the fundamental facts about our energy picture, then and now. In part 2 I provide you with basic background information on the wide array of alternative and renewable energy forms available, along with their pros and cons. Part 3 is where you kick-start the planning process for the People's Energy Plan by evaluating your personal energy use, which will give you a good feel for the variables involved in creating an umbrella national plan. In the back of the book you'll find additional helpful material, including web links, references, a glossary of energy terms, and recommended reading.

Another resource that will inspire you to get involved in creating the People's Energy Plan for America is *The Grand Energy Transition* (*The GET*), a powerful new documentary film released in 2012. Based on the book of the same name by Robert Hefner III, founder and owner of GHK Exploration, who pioneered deep and ultra-deep natural gas exploration, *The GET* forecasts the continuing decline of coal and oil, and predicts the coming "Age of Energy Gases." In Hefner's opinion, America's abundant natural gas will serve as the major bridge to this new energy age, along with wind and solar power, to create a new, hydrogen-based economy. The film was directed by Emmy award winner Greg Mellott and produced by Gray Frederickson, who won an Oscar for coproducing *The Godfather: Part II*. To learn more about *The GET*, visit www.The-GET.com.

As you can already tell, encouraging the people of America to take up the cause of energy independence has become a passion of mine, so as you join in this journey, I'd like to hear from you. Just send me an email at info@energyadvocates.org. I also welcome you to visit www.EnergyAdvocates.org, where you can get informational materials on the subject as well as a bumper sticker sharing our message that, now more than ever, "America Needs America's Energy." Future generations are depending on us to keep the American dream alive.

Notes for the Introduction

1. Gingrich, Newt. Introduction to *Drill Here, Drill Now, Pay Less*. Washington, DC: Regnery Publishing, Inc. 2008.
2. Clinton, Bill. *Back to Work*. New York: Knopf Publishing. 2011. p. 142.
3. Huckabee, Mike. *A Simple Government*. New York: Sentinel HC. 2011. p. 120.
4. US Senate. February 15, 1985. Committee on Energy and Natural Resources. *Impact of Treasury Department Tax Reform Proposal on Oil and Gas Industry.*

Please use this space to make notes about this chapter for later reference.

Part I

Energy Perspectives, Then and Now

American Energy
and the Global Situation

"We must not look to government to solve our problems"
—**President Ronald Reagan**

To understand the trajectory of the energy industry in America, you need to know something about the forces that drive it. In *The Braking Point* I explained the six moving parts that influence the market and ultimately impact the price of the energy you consume:

- Peaking Production
- Increasing Demand for Oil or Energy
- Decreasing Refinery Capacity
- Terrorism and Energy Security
- Inadequate Government Policy
- Misinformation about the Industry

At the time *The Braking Point* was published, my capable coauthor Jason P. Reimbold interviewed two global experts in the energy industry who provided their perspective on variables that can impact energy dynamics in this country.

The first authority was leading world oil industry analyst Charlie Maxwell, who offered insights on the current state of affairs and expectations on where the energy industry might be by 2035. He asserted that if demand continued to outstrip supply, there might eventually be a *free-for-all* among nations. Since many governments cannot institute price controls, rationing by price would likely be the most viable mechanism for all countries. In Maxwell's view, alternative fuel sources would not become a major factor in the foreseeable future because the cost to produce them is so high, and the allocation of such capacity to energy production adversely affects manufacturing's ability to produce goods. Maxwell further predicted that oil would remain the dominant energy source until 2035, when natural gas might supersede it.

The second noted interview was with His Royal Highness Reza Pahlavi, who fled Iran in 1979 after the Islamic Revolution. In addition to a strong revenue stream from its oil exports, Iran contains the second largest estimated reserves of natural gas in the world. In Pahlavi's opinion, however, Iran has failed to keep pace with modernization of its oil and gas sector because the regime has cut off foreign capital inflow from the major oil companies. In the ensuing years, two generations of young Iranians who have reached maturity are deeply dissatisfied with the economic inequality and lack of material advantages that are available in Western societies. He believed that reestablishment of foreign investment could only be achieved with political and economic stability, as well as a professional, ethical management force in the country's energy sector. Pahlavi pointed out that under such conditions, and in concert with new technologies enabling easier long-distance transport of natural gas, Iran's potentially significant natural gas exports could position it to assume a leading role in OPEC, encouraging the cartel to support the spirit of partnership with both energy producers and consuming nations.

Looking back, our two experts were right on the mark. As Maxwell foresaw, oil remains the dominant source of energy in our country today. Whether his prediction will hold true through 2035 depends on changes in attitude toward natural gas. If Compressed Natural Gas (CNG) vehicles come into play, both in terms of fleets and transportation vehicles across the country, that would impact oil's role in the mix. His view that price will serve as the rationing mechanism has also proven true at this stage. However, the higher oil prices go, the more natural gas looks like a good economic alternative, which could also be a factor in the length of oil's dominance.

Pahlavi's take on Iran's future is looking more correct every day. Young people there are not willing to accept the status quo, and despite harsh regime measures against protesters, the nation's political and economic instability will give sway sooner or later. The Iranian people want a democracy and free market of sorts, so Pahlavi's forecast of the coming changes that will impact Iran's role in OPEC appears inevitable. The direction he anticipates his native country heading could bring welcome change to longtime energy security threats emanating from that region of the Middle East.

Peaking Production

Then: In 1970 the US government reported that the US had reached its peak in oil production. From 1970 to 1978 the government continued to assert that oil production had topped out in this country. As previously mentioned, in 1978 President Carter echoed these dire predictions and pushed through the Fuel Use Act, arguing that we did not possess enough natural gas to meet the country's needs and would have to rely on coal, instead. Ironically, some of America's leading energy companies concurred with this finding, and as a result, exploration for both oil and gas in this country came to a standstill. Instead of moving forward, our energy situation took a backward turn.

Now: America today has been proven to possess an abundance of both oil and gas. In 1978 Prudhoe Bay in Alaska was discovered, and the Trans-Alaska Pipeline eventually produced over a half a million barrels of oil per day. Recently, Harold Hamm of Oklahoma's

Continental Resources, along with other independent operators, discovered enough oil in North Dakota's Bakken shale formation to equal the reserves of Saudi Arabia. The Bakken Play represents a tectonic shift in American energy and the global situation. Our country has long been dependent on foreign oil, to the point where we were importing 60 percent of all our petroleum and were on track to hit 70 percent in this decade. Thanks to the Bakken Play, which is mainly oil, our dependency on foreign oil has already dropped to around the 50 percent mark. This game-changer turns the global situation in our favor. Despite this move in the right direction, however, we cannot afford to let up in our national quest to achieve total energy independence. It would only take a political crisis like Iran blocking the Strait of Hormuz to hold a percentage of our oil hostage and drive oil prices up. Our energy security still needs to be addressed through development of a comprehensive domestic energy policy.

Increasing Demand

Then: According to estimates by the Energy Information Administration (EIA) in 2008, over the next twenty years America's demand for oil would increase by 30 percent, close to double the present level. As consumption surged, US production was expected to continue its decline. In 1970 the United States imported 36 percent of total consumption of petroleum. As of 2006, America imported nearly 60 percent of its daily consumption. If we failed to meet the challenge, it was projected that by 2020 we could rely on foreign governments for nearly 70 percent of our oil, a dependency that would present our country with even greater security risks than it faces today.

Now: As economic conditions improve, the BRIC countries (Brazil, Russia, India, and China), as well as other nations, will begin consuming more oil. As their consumption grows, demand will pick up. Chart 2 shows projected oil consumption from 2011 to 2035 by OECD (Organization for Economic Development and Cooperation) countries and non-OECD countries.

Chart 2

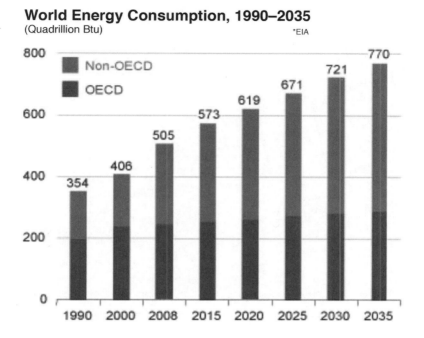

World Energy Consumption, 1990–2035
(Quadrillion Btu)   *EIA

Given this escalating growth rate of projected consumption, the challenge here in the US will be an ability to keep pace, not only to meet our own country's demand for oil, but to export our energy expertise to help other countries become more energy self-sufficient.

Then: In 2008 many of the same issues facing demand for oil confronted the future of natural gas. America's demand for natural gas was projected to rise even faster than oil. If Department of Energy (DOE) projections were correct, by 2020 Americans would consume 62 percent more natural gas than we did at that time. The EIA also estimated that approximately 40 percent of potential gas reserves were located on federal lands either closed to exploration or severely restricted.

Now: It is critical that we preserve the environment. However, as Chart 3 clearly shows, there are many enormous tracts of land currently restricted from natural gas production in the lower forty-eight states, including offshore sites.

Chart 3

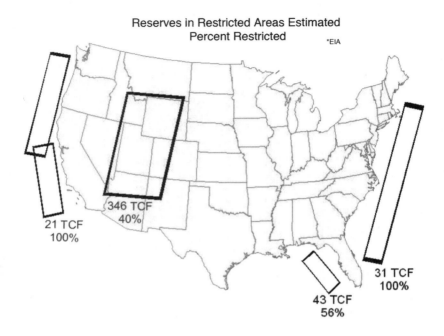

By opening these particular areas in a proper way and protecting the environment, we can ensure America becomes more self-reliant and energy-independent.

Then: Due to the economic meltdown in 2008, commodity prices were down 50 percent, demand for manufactured products was severely impacted, world GDP was shrinking for the first time in sixty years, and world trade was forecasted to shrink by 9 percent that year, the largest decline in eight decades. According to the *Wall Street Journal*, the Baltic Dry Index (BDI), a strong indicator of demand for energy, was on the downside. The BDI is considered a leading economic indicator because it shows the number of shipments of goods being transported, either as imports or exports. If the BDI is slowing, it reflects a downturn in the economy.

If the BDI is trending up, it means more demand for oil. When nations start transporting more items, such as computers or lumber, it begins the demand circle of life—from shipping a product, to using it, then to recycling it. Since it takes several months for products to get from point A to point B, the BDI serves as a good gauge for the energy industry to properly evaluate where the market is heading in a three- to six-month time frame and plan for increased demand by hiring and training more workers and increasing refining capacity.

Now: Based on *Bloomberg* data in October 2011, the BDI rose to a high as rents for panamax cargo vessels (the largest ships capable of passing through the Panama Canal locks) climbed the most in a week since May of 2011.[1] However, in the first half of 2012 the BDI had begun to plummet.

Terrorism and Security

Then: In 2008 the US Energy Information Administration (EIA) outlined the strategic importance and associated threats facing each oil-exporting country, some of which provide us with petroleum:

- **Algeria:** Armed militants have confronted government forces
- **Bolivia:** Large reserves of natural gas; exports may be delayed due to new laws unfriendly to foreigners
- **Caspian Sea:** BTC pipeline now open; many ethnic conflicts; high expectation of future oil production in the region; no maritime border agent
- **Caucasus Region 2:** Strategic transit area for natural gas and oil pipelines
- **Columbia:** Destabilizing force in South America; oil exports subject to attack by protesters; armed militants
- **Ecuador:** Unstable politically; protests threaten oil exports
- **Indonesia:** No longer a net exporter; separatist movements; peacekeeping force in place; violence threat to Strait of Malacca
- **Iran:** No direct exports to US but exports 2.5 million barrels daily to other world markets
- **Iraq:** From 2003 to 2005 there were 236 attacks on the oil infrastructure

- **Libya:** Newly restored diplomatic relations; Western IOCs not awarded contracts in send EPSA Round
- **Nigeria:** High rate of violence and crime; large income disparity; tribal and ethnic conflict and protests have repeatedly suspended oil shipments
- **Russia:** Second only to South America in oil production; Yukos Oil Affair has bred uncertain investment climate
- **Saudi Arabia:** Long-term stability of al-Saud family; Western oil workers subject to attacks
- **Sudan:** Darfur Crisis and North-South internal conflict threatens government stability; security of oil transport at risk
- **Venezuela:** Large exporter to the US; President Chavez frequently threatens to divert those exports and nationalize the resource base

Now: Most of the potential security threats in these countries remain and in some cases have heightened. More threats in other areas of the world have also surfaced. For instance, if Iran attempts to close the Strait of Hormuz, our energy security is in jeopardy from the standpoint of price and supply. In addition to the threats already mentioned, America faces potential internal terrorist attacks and cyber-security threats on our energy infrastructure that could wreak havoc on the citizenry and imperil national security.

These multifarious threats to our energy security, both external and internal, argue even more strenuously for the goal of total energy independence. By that, we mean total freedom from reliance on energy sources questionable to our national interests. Keep in mind that we have Canada and Mexico, two friendly allies who also produce oil, so if we have a certain percent of energy imported from them, that is not an issue. The goal is to replace all foreign oil from countries with even a question of being hostile to us or of being in an alliance with us.

Inadequate Government Policy

Then: The 2008 economic stimulus package passed by the US Congress set aside $21.5 billion for scientific research, as well as $5 billion for weatherization of houses, $11 billion for updating the electric grid, and $2 billion for advanced automobile battery technology. Additional grants and funds were also made available for other energy projects.

Now: Instead of launching us further into energy independence, government involvement has set us back economically, as well as leaving us even more dependent on foreign energy sources. It's one thing for the government to experiment and fail. But when a company like Solyndra is up and running for just a year or two, spends over $500 million, and then goes bankrupt, that is not proper use of our funds when we are in an economic downturn. As the *Wall Street Journal* noted in September 2011, the $535 million Solyndra scandal is just one in a string of failures, with the Department of Energy shoveling out over $1 billion in new loan guarantees to solar projects in Nevada and Arizona, and more deals pending.[2]

The US government needs to focus on areas like better technology for natural gas. Hydraulic fracturing is important, but we need better technology to ensure everything is maintained environmentally. For example, Schlumberger is a service company involved in putting proper water treatment in place in areas undergoing hydraulic fracturing. So we are starting to see technology that complements what we are already doing, instead of just handing out over $500 million as was done with Solyndra and seeing if some new product pans out.

Government assistance and money could also have been used more beneficially in rebuilding energy infrastructure. In this case, a public–private partnership is necessary. For example, if we would have put that $500 million into building Compressed Natural Gas (CNG) fueling stations, it would have been a great shot in the arm for the natural gas sector and the energy business overall. We could have started with government fleets nationwide, but it would also have extended into the public arena. Today, many UPS trucks, as well as public buses in

Los Angeles, are CNG-fueled. The benefits are enormous: The cost of CNG fuel is roughly 50 percent less than the $3.50 to $4.00 per gallon for normal gasoline, and in some areas of the country, even lower than that. CNG is also an environmental plus, as it burns much cleaner and is better for the engine as well.

The TransCanada Corp's Keystone XL Pipeline is a perfect example of government policy working against our energy independence. On the one hand, our government said yes to Solyndra, but no to permitting the Keystone pipeline, which is a privately funded project. Keystone could not only have provided twenty thousand jobs in a down economy, saving taxpayer dollars on unemployment, but more importantly, it could have helped make us less dependent on our enemies for oil. Worse yet, instead of building that pipeline within the lower forty-eight states that would have transported 700,000 barrels of crude a day to refineries in the US Gulf Coast, TransCanada is now thinking of constructing it through its western territories and exporting that oil to China.

Misinformation About the Industry

Then: For years the public perception of the energy industry has been that of fat cats, ruthless J. R. Ewing types who make a killing off oil in their own backyard. Other pervasive myths about the industry include a belief that oil companies do not pay their fair share of taxes, that they make windfall profits and are "colossal giants" owned by a ruthless group of "them," that the industry gouges the consumer, and that energy companies destroy the environment and endanger species.

Now: When it comes to the stereotype of J. R. Ewing, nothing could be further from the truth. Today, thousands of individuals in this country operate marginal wells—those producing ten barrels a day or less—that not only provide these people with a living, but also account for nearly 60 percent of our domestic production. What's more, in Pennsylvania's Marcellus shale formation, hundreds of mineral and royalty owners are now benefitting financially from oil and gas lease bonuses. This relatively new exploration activity also accounts for 72,000 new jobs in Pennsylvania since 2009.

The idea that energy companies do not pay their fair share of taxes is another bogus idea. Most consumers do not realize that the average gasoline pump price in 2011 included a whopping 45¢ per gallon just in government (federal and state) taxes, which are supposed to be placed in the Highway Trust Fund for construction and repair of roads and bridges. The energy industry also pays severance taxes, gross production taxes, and ad valorem taxes, not to mention corporate taxes on the company's income each year.

The gross production tax levied on the industry accounts for 10 percent or more of total state tax collections each year. Over the last three years the gross production tax has averaged nearly $1 billion per year in Oklahoma alone. Gross production taxes are apportioned across state revenue funds that support county roads, local schools, higher education, and general revenue. In addition, there are 71,224 Oklahomans directly employed by the drilling and production sectors and another 228,115 jobs supported indirectly by the oil and gas industry. These approximately 300,000 jobs generate more than $14 billion in labor income in Oklahoma. A 2009 analysis showed an energy industry whose annual operations generate $51.7 billion in Oklahoma goods and services, almost one-third of Oklahoma's gross state product.

As for allegedly windfall profits, the most recent data compiled by the American Petroleum Institute indicates that US oil and gas companies made an average of 9.5¢ on every dollar of sales in the second quarter of 2011, compared with 10¢ per dollar of sales for all manufacturing. According to Yahoo! Finance, of the top 114 industries according to net profit margin, independent oil and gas ranked number 80 with 8.3 percent, along with health insurance at 8.1 percent, and aerospace and defense at 6.6 percent. At the top of the list were periodical publishing at 51.7 percent, application software at 22.7 percent, cigarettes at 19.8 percent, beer brewing at 16.5 percent, wine and distilling at 14.9 percent, soft drinks at 14.3 percent, wireless at 14.1 percent, PCs at 13.9 percent, and entertainment at 12.5 percent.

Few Americans also know that until a few years ago the energy industry struggled through a twenty-year depression. Profit margins were below the average of other industries, and well-known companies disappeared due to financial failures or mergers. Employees were hit hard as more than 350,000 men and women (52 percent of the industry workforce) had to seek career employment elsewhere. Oil and gas operators of record from 1974 to 1999 experienced an 84 percent decline from peak. A 2007 university study concluded that close to 50 percent of the petroleum engineers working then would be retiring within the next five years.

Another popular misconception is that energy companies are "colossal giants" owned by "them." From a sheer market value perspective, however, several years ago Royal-Dutch, Anadarko, Marathon, and Devon could not compare to Wal-Mart or Apple. Of the top fifty US companies listed by Yahoo! Finance under the category of market value today, only four are oil and gas–related companies. Under their category of the top fifty US companies ranked by equity, only five are oil and gas–related companies. In terms of ownership, the largest percentage of shareholders of energy companies are institutional investors, whose business includes managing pension funds for companies and government employees such as teachers and police. For example, in 2004 ExxonMobil Corp's shareholder breakdown was as follows: top institutional fundholder, Barclay's Bank at 4.25 percent; top mutual fund holders, Vanguard Index 500 Fund at 0.91 percent and the College Retirement Equities Fund and Stock Account at 0.74 percent.

The perception that oil companies gouge people at the pump is another myth based on lack of information by the consumer. In 2005 an average gallon of gasoline cost $2.51, but when compared to the average cost per gallon of the following consumer goods, this was low:

- milk: $2.99
- Coca-Cola: $2.84
- Gatorade: $5.20
- Evian water: $5.60
- orange juice: $6.64
- Crisco oil: $7.44
- Perrier water: $8.16
- Snapple: $10.32
- Scope mouthwash: $27.20
- olive oil: $51.04
- real maple syrup: $57.08
- Jack Daniel's whiskey: $101.12
- Visine eye drops: $995.84
- Nasacort nasal spray: $2,615.28

Even in 2012, when an average gallon of gasoline cost between $3 and $4 (including taxes), the price was still reasonable in comparison to a gallon of milk at $4-plus or a gallon of Tide laundry detergent at $22.99.

Lastly, the big bogeyman of myths about the energy industry is that oil and gas companies destroy the environment. Far from that image, today's energy companies are in the forefront of environmental protection and increasingly finding that exploration and wildlife preservation can not only peacefully coexist but in some cases be mutually beneficial. For instance, Alaska Governor Sean Parnell testified to the House Resources Committee in September 2011 that Prudhoe Bay, located sixty miles west of ANWR, has been operating for over thirty years and produced more than sixteen billion barrels of oil so far. Amidst that activity, the Central Arctic caribou herd at Prudhoe Bay has grown from 5,000 in 1975 to over 67,000 in 2008. This rarely reported good news is due to the heat of the crude passing through the pipeline, which warms the tundra topsoil, causing grasses to sprout where they had never grown before. As a consequence, caribou herds and other wildlife have not only survived, but thrived.

While there will always be companies that fail to live up to standard, the energy industry as a whole is committed to ensuring that regulations are followed to the strictest degree by all its members. Even after the April 2010 BP oil spill off the coast of Louisiana, dire predictions about harm to the ocean ecosystem for the next twenty-five years turned out way off-base. Less than two years after the disaster, environmental marine effects from the spill are all but gone, thanks to mother nature's amazing ability to heal herself.

Notes for Chapter 1

1. *Bloomberg News.* October 7, 2011.
2. *Wall Street Journal.* September 19, 2011.

Please use this space to make notes about this chapter
for later reference.

America's Energy Dreams: Transportation

"The word 'energy' incidentally equates with the Greek word for 'challenge.' I think there is much to learn in thinking of our federal energy problems in that light. Further, it is important for us to think of energy in terms of a gift of life."

—Thomas P. Carr
Testimony to the US Senate Commerce Committee
September 1974

Nothing moves without energy! When it comes to transportation, Americans rely on gasoline and diesel fuel, which means 90 percent of the energy to move comes from oil. It is always good to be diversified in life, however, and that includes our sources of energy. The arrival of more CNG vehicles on the road will help to balance that reliance by using a much cheaper fuel and one that is also cleaner. We are not just looking at an economic driver at work in turning to different fuel sources for transportation needs, but environmental balance as well. If we continue to rely solely on oil or using fossil fuels alone, the environmental impact will exist in the form of our carbon footprint.

Decreasing Refinery Capacity

Then: When talking about transportation in the United States in 2008, the first thing that came to the mind of most consumers was gasoline. However, a very important factor was also diesel. More diesel was being imported into this country as a percentage than gasoline. Both of these fuels required refining, however, and the refining capacity in this country had been declining at a steady rate despite ever-increasing demand. Even four years prior *USA Today* warned, "Motorists face gasoline shortages as well as record prices the next few weeks because of the skintight US refining and distribution network. The vulnerability of that network, combined with low inventories of both gasoline and crude oil from which it's made, have the government and energy experts increasingly nervous that some places in the USA will run out of gas temporarily."

Now: As Chart 4 indicates, refining capacity in America has continued to decline, with no foreseeable improvement right into 2014.

Chart 4

US Number of Operating Refineries
* EIA 2010

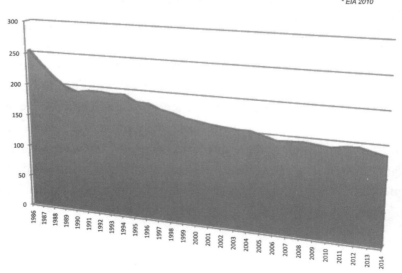

Although there are 148 operable refineries in the US today, no significant (or sophisticated) new refinery has been constructed in the US since 1978 when one was built in Garyville, Indiana. One "new" refinery began operating in 2008 in Douglas, Wyoming, but its capacity is limited. Capacity has also been added to existing refineries through upgrades or new construction. For example, in 1998 Orion Refinery massively upgraded and reopened a refinery in Norco, Louisiana.

A primary reason that a significant crude oil refinery has not been opened since 1978 is environmental requirements and permitting. US refineries had been operating at record-high levels (up to 98 percent of capacity) to produce the fuels that consumers needed. Many companies were exporting their refining capacity and storage elsewhere, and shipping already-refined petroleum productions to the United States. When the cost of gasoline increases, it is primarily due to refiners paying higher prices for crude oil. Higher tanker freight rates, low European inventories, and more stringent US fuel specifications also contribute to gasoline prices. Refineries and petrochemical plants bear a heavy tax burden as well.

The importance of refineries to our energy needs for transportation cannot be understated. Most consumers have no idea that a percentage of the price per gallon paid at the pump goes toward refining, marketing, and transporting that fuel to gas stations. At present, the demand for gasoline has dropped almost 10 percent since 2008, primarily due to current global economic conditions. With US refineries producing more gasoline, diesel, and jet fuel than the country presently needs, the US is now exporting a record amount of gasoline. Yet at the same time the US continues to import well over half of the crude oil it uses. As the economy recovers and demand grows again, America will have to invest millions of dollars just to maintain refining facilities so that current capacity will be available for consumption.

Some argue that the persistent decrease in refining capacity is a function of technological advances in equipment and refining techniques, and according to industry leaders, efficiencies realized in the last few years have created the equivalent of a new medium-sized refinery every year. Still, the underlying truth is that even with these efficiencies, the demand for petroleum products has and will continue to outpace the performance and creation of efficient means of production with no foreseeable end to this trend.

Major Supply and Demand Factors Contributing to Gasoline Prices, Then and Now

- **High demand:** Continuing high demand in America by consumers is for transportation needs.
- **Low inventories:** To keep up with this demand, energy companies must have inventories, but that requires a continuous supply of oil and gas, which cannot be produced overnight. Companies must first drill, transport oil or gas to refineries and gas plants, and then maintain it in sufficient quantities in reserves. America's Strategic Petroleum Reserve, which was created after the Oil Embargo of 1973, only holds enough oil in underground storage to last this country from thirty to forty days.
- **Supply snags:** An oil embargo, such as the Arab Oil Embargo from 1973 to 1974, causes a major disruption in oil supply to this country. During that period, gasoline was rationed at the pump, with the government forcing drivers to fuel on alternate days based on their license plate numbers. Another big factor affecting our supply of oil is weather-related events, such as hurricanes or earthquakes, which can destroy refineries. Geopolitical crises, including war, can also cause a cutoff in oil imports.
- **Economic disruption:** An event like the 2008 economic meltdown hurts the energy business because the resulting decrease in demand by consumers and manufacturers forces energy companies to lay off employees. The energy business needs a planning window sometimes of several years, so economic cycles can have a huge effect in terms of making

a determination whether it is the right time to rehire, train, invest in technology, etc.

- **Cartel crunch:** OPEC decides how much oil they will produce on a daily basis, and whether they will increase or decrease that amount. The current supply of such oil on the market greatly affects the price we pay at the pump here in the US.

- **The fear factor:** Environmental concerns that result in bureaucratic red tape or prolonged legal battles are one fear factor that can impact the cost of fuel. Terrorism threats are another.

- **Vulnerable infrastructure:** America's energy infrastructure is antiquated and not up to standard today. Government policy has consistently refused to address this problem, which leads to higher prices for the consumer. Instead of deferring maintenance, we need to invest now in our energy infrastructure to help reduce consumer costs and ensure a continued energy supply for future generations.

Please use this space to make notes about this chapter
for later reference.

3

America's Energy Dreams: Power Generation

"Alternative energy is a future idea whose time is past. Renewable energy is a future idea whose time is come."

—**Bill Penden**
Atlas World Press Review
April 1977

In *The Braking Point* I recalled that after a presentation I made in Cushing, Oklahoma—the pipeline crossroads of America—about the energy challenges facing our nation, someone in the audience stated to me, "I don't know what you are worried about. If we run out of oil and gas we'll still have electricity." Unfortunately, this is a widespread misconception among American consumers who do not realize that electric generation requires energy. Those power generation sources can include natural gas, coal, wind, and other alternative forms of energy.

Then: Four years ago, various means of power generation were being touted as the next cure, including the popular ones of wind and nuclear fission. These alone were not overnight solutions, as was the case for alternative energies.

At that point in time in the US, renewable and alternative energies made up approximately 6 percent of total energy consumed. Biomass and hydroelectric accounted for nearly all of the alternative fuels then available. US ethanol production was about 500,000 barrels a day, and in 2008, a $799 million ethanol producer filed for bankruptcy. Solar, wind, and geothermal alternatives contributed less than 10 percent of the energy mix. The cost to upgrade just Oklahoma's transmission grid had been estimated to cost over $3 billion. Wind was being touted as a big part of the energy solution. But it was also noted that a decline in wind energy, coupled with cold weather and increased energy use, led to an electric emergency that caused the Texas grid operator to cut service to some large Houston-area customers in February 2008. Wind power needs a backup fuel supply that can be switched on when little or no wind exists. Natural gas is the only fuel that can serve as backup to avoid an intermittent power supply when relying on wind for electricity. Due to the intermittent nature of wind power, there is the need for backup power generating capacity, which is largely dependent on natural gas and, in some cases, coal.[1]

Aging nuclear plants had become another concern. The Nuclear Regulatory Commission (NRC) was analyzing eleven sites, including the one closest to Oklahoma in Wolf Creek, Kansas (Oklahoma was one of sixteen states without a nuclear plant). The NRC also had more than thirty new reactor applications. At that time approximately half of the 104 currently operating reactors faced license expirations in the next three years. In the meantime, France had fifty-eight nuclear energy plants providing over 75 percent of that country's electricity. Japan also relied on nuclear power for 30 percent of its electricity.

In 2008 "clean coal" technologies were making headlines, but the technologies were not being implemented in a broad sense. The main goal of clean coal was to reduce emissions, with strong emphasis on the capture and storage of CO_2. Though clean coal efforts were marching forward, there was still a need for research and development, along with valid implementation of clean coal technologies. The main emphasis at the time for use of coal was its economic advantage. Lower energy costs, which help economically challenged families and senior citizens, along with the fact that electricity was a relative bargain among energy products, were the coal industry's primary arguments for continued reliance on coal in America as an affordable energy source.

As of 2008, no one method had proven a measurable addition to the energy mix. Despite technological advances at that stage, the economics of producing alternative fuels were challenging. In fact, the EIA projected alternative fuels to account for less than 10 percent of the total energy mix by 2030. Therefore, conventional energies were expected to remain the dominant sources of fuel for some time.

Now: We don't yet have a good balance of sources that can get us to our goal of total energy independence. We are still using many forms of energy, as Chart 5 shows.

Chart 5

US Energy Consumption by Source, 2010
(Source: EIA)

BIOMASS 4.4% *renewable* Heating, electricity, transportation	**PETROLEUM** 36.7% *nonrenewable* Transportation, manufacturing	
HYDROPOWER 2.6% *renewable* Electricity	**NATURAL GAS** 25.1% *nonrenewable* Heating, manufacturing, electricity	
GEOTHERMAL 0.2% *renewable* Heating, electricity	**COAL** 21.2% *nonrenewable* Electricity, manufacturing	
WIND 0.7% *renewable* Electricity	**URANIUM** 8.6% *nonrenewable* Electricity	
SOLAR & OTHER 0.1% *renewable* Light, heating, electricity		

Although certain energy sectors are more predominant than others, there is room for natural gas and renewables to grow, and an opportunity for biomass exists. In terms of nuclear energy, however, as a result of the Fukushima Daiichi nuclear complex disaster in Japan, public confidence in this form of power generation has dropped. It was reported at one time that Japan was considering shutting down all of its nuclear reactors by the end of 2012.[2]

Notes for Chapter 3
1. *Wall Street Journal.* August 12, 2011.
2. *Wall Street Journal.* January 7, 2012.

Please use this space to make notes about this chapter for later reference.

4

Global Economic Realities

"We are now spending half a trillion dollars on foreign oil, importing 62 percent of the oil we use, and we haven't had the leadership in DC to do anything about it. We've got to move to other sources of energy. But we've gotten way behind, and will continue to pay the fiddler. It's not a good future."

—T. Boone Pickens

Then: In 2008 the BRIC countries (Brazil, Russia, India, and China) were the focus, with economic experts predicting they would become the growing powers of the twenty-first century. As the world's consumption continued to increase, analysts thought it might be difficult for current levels of production to satisfy demand. The International Energy Agency (IEA) published estimates showing world energy demand increasing by 60 percent as early as 2030. As the BRIC nations continued to grow economically, their consumption of energy would increase correspondingly. In particular, the GDP per capita of the developing nations of China (at $5,000) and India (at $2,900) had yet to reach the relatively low GDP per capita of Mexico (at $9,000).

This expected rise in the GDP per capita set the stage for vast increases in demand for energy. For example, from 2000 to 2005 India and China increased their energy consumption by 15 percent and 42 percent, respectively. China at that point had 1.3 billion people with approximately thirty million cars. As globalization continued to evolve and provide the people of China new opportunities, their purchasing power and capacity for consumption grew correspondingly. China was expected to have as big a car market as the US by 2015 and possibly surpass us in capacity by 2035. Chinese demand for autos in the first quarter of 2008 showed sales up sharply, despite the stock market slump and inflation on the rise. About 2.6 million vehicles were sold in China in the first quarter of 2008. This boom added considerable pressure on reserves. Further exploration would be needed to be able to satisfy this growing giant.

As the demand for energy increased, oil would continue to dominate the energy mix. Considering the EIA estimates cited above, it was important to note that while wind, geothermal, and additional alternative renewable energies showed a small increase, the lag time for implementation of these alternatives could hinder their effectiveness to help meet energy demands in the near and intermediate future.

In the early 1990s I was part of a delegation that met with the minister of energy of Russia. We were told that the Russian government had identified 35,000 idle wells in need of repair. Unfortunately, those conditions still existed in 2008. We were definitely at the braking point, because demand would return. This outdated and inefficient infrastructure was making it even more difficult to meet the demand for energy that existed at that time.

There was also Brazil, which at that time was a world leader in biofuel and ethanol production. The ethanol Brazil produced primarily came from sugar cane. However, in 2007 US Energy Secretary Samuel Bodman stated that corn-based ethanol was contributing to higher food prices and advised the US to begin moving away from ethanol made from food.

Peaking Production

In *The Braking Point* I told how in 1975, while working for then-US Senator Dewey F. Bartlett, I first realized what a real force OPEC was in the energy industry. Senator Bartlett had asked several of his staff members, including me, to review remarks he was planning to make in Norway to OPEC officials. Only a year before, the energy industry had been deeply impacted by the 1973–1974 oil embargo. It was obvious that the energy industry and our nation's petroleum security would be important issues to deal with during my lifetime.

I also noted that in 2005 investment banker Matt Simmons had written a book, *Twilight in the Desert,* in which he discussed the possibilities of the oncoming Saudi oil shock. Unlike the US, members of OPEC do not adhere to a standardized form of reporting on oil production figures, and given the strained relationship between OPEC and the rest of the world, some analysts speculated that their reserves were overstated. Some even asserted that Saudi Arabian oil production had already peaked or was near peaking. If this were the case, we could be closer to the braking point than was realized.

Much of the concern with Saudi oil production was centered on the world's largest oil field. With the world looking to the Kingdom of Saudi Arabia and the Middle East for oil, the balance between their interests and that of our country was very delicate. In the last fifty years, the US had turned abroad for other sources of oil, most notably the Middle East. According to *Oil and Gas Journal,* the Middle East possessed nearly 62 percent of the world's known oil reserves, making it the center of attention in the eyes of the world.

Now: China is already taking 38 percent more oil from the Middle East than the US.[1] According to the *Wall Street Journal,* investment in North America accelerated from zero to 34 percent by the end of 2011. Experts believe that high prices for energy are inevitable, and while the global recession has eased oil demand, it was climbing again now that the economy was recovering. China today is importing 20 percent more oil than it did just one year ago.[2]

Demand also continues at a rapid pace. China's electricity consumption is projected to nearly triple over the next decade, growing by an average of over 4 percent per year. South Sudan is increasing its energy imports and also blocking its oil exports to meet its own demand.[3]

Then: In 2008 the US led the world in importing, followed by Japan, China, Germany, and South Korea. Top exporters included Saudi Arabia, followed by Russia, the United Arab Emirates, Norway, and Iran.

Now: Chart 6 lists the top world exporters in 2009, showing how reliant the world is today on the top three nations, Saudi Arabia, Russian, and Iran—all of which are politically unstable.

Chart 6

Top World Oil Net Exporters, 2010		
(thousand barrels per day)		
Rank	Country	Exports
1	Saudi Arabia	7,300
2	Russia	7,007
3	Iran	2,407
4	United Arab Emirates	2,270
5	Norway	2,125
6	Kuwait	2,124
7	Nigeria	1,939
8	Angola	1,874
9	Algeria	1,773
10	Iraq	1,764
11	Venezuela	1,719
12	Libya	1,525
13	Kazakhstan	1,299
14	Canada	1,159
15	Qatar	1,077

EIA 2010

Interestingly, the US exports almost one million barrels of oil a day, largely in the form of petroleum products. Chart 7 showing the top world consumers of oil in 2010 makes a strong case for America moving to energy independence.

Chart 7

Top World Oil Consumers, 2010		
(thousand barrels per day)		
Rank	Country	Consumption
1	United States	19,180
2	China	8,371
3	Japan	4,452
4	India	3,215
5	Russia	2,686
6	Saudi Arabia	2,676
7	Brazil	2,599
8	Germany	2,495
9	Korea, South	2,251
10	Canada	2,208
11	Mexico	2,073
12	Iran	1,898
13	France	1,861
14	United Kingdom	1,622
15	Italy	1,528

* EIA 2010

We are the leading consumer of oil, followed by China and Japan. A country like Japan, however, which does not produce oil or gas, is still less dependent than we are, despite the fact that we possess abundant natural resources that, if developed, could suffice for our demand.

A Global Reality: The India Example

Then: With the fourth largest economy in the world, India was still a relatively new frontier for oil and gas exploration. The Indian oil and gas industry had suffered from sizable underinvestment, which led to the subcontinent's frenzied quest for energy. Despite significant governmental policy changes since the late 1990s, India had been unable to attract exploration and production (E&P) activity from the supermajor international oil companies. Sizable offshore opportunities across the globe had been the focus of the supermajors for some time, which made India's onshore possibilities appear as an inequitable pursuit. However, this opening translated into immense opportunities for smaller independents.

Since India's implementation of the New Exploration Licensing Program (NELP), numerous significant onshore discoveries have been made in India, including a potential billion barrel discovery made by a joint venture. India's economic growth and expanding need for natural resources had encouraged changes in policies that had limited the subcontinent's exploration for oil and gas. Specifically, the government of India had taken progressive action to attract foreign investment and soften the budgetary restrictions that E&P companies faced in the 1990s. These proactive policies were evidenced by the expansion of oil and gas licensing. The plan of a Hydrocarbon Vision 2025 and NELP provided the foundation for India's surging oil and gas industry. India's turnabout was a stunning example of how proper governmental policies encourage the needed development of a nation's resources.

Now: India is continuing its frantic quest for energy. A friendly environment for oil and gas ventures remains, with all three areas mentioned in *The Braking Point* in play today: local exploration, plans for strategic acquisition of foreign energy assets, and exploration opportunities in countries that the US considers unstable. Even though government policies that encourage needed development of the nation's resources are now in place, India is still far behind where it needs to be to achieve energy independence.

As Chart 8 shows, India's energy demand continues to rise, primarily due to vehicle purchases.

Chart 8

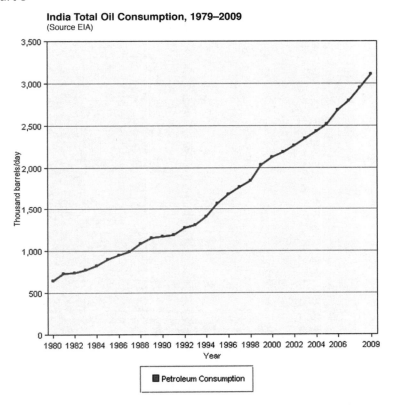

India Total Oil Consumption, 1979–2009
(Source EIA)

In 2010 India consumed 3.2 million barrels of oil per day. The nation's resource base is substantial, but the country relies on imports for most of its energy use. *Oil and Gas Journal* reports that as of January 2011 India had approximately 5.7 billion barrels of proven oil reserves, the second-largest amount in the Asia-Pacific region after China.

Despite this position, India was the world's fifth largest net importer of oil in 2010 with more than 2.2 million barrels per day, or about 70 percent of its consumption imported from the Middle East. India continues to work toward deregulation of the hydrocarbons industry and to encourage foreign investment. Oil and Natural Gas Corporation (ONGC) accounted for almost three-fourths of India's oil production in 2009 and 2010.

Chart 9

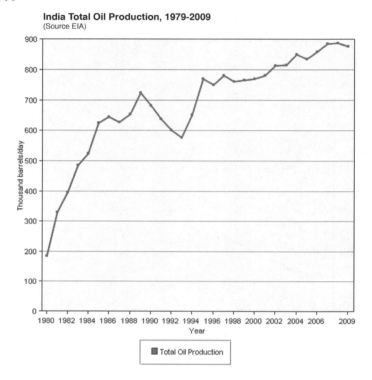

India Total Oil Production, 1979-2009
(Source EIA)

The Indian Oil Corporation, the largest state-owned company in the downstream sector, operates eight of India's twenty-one refineries. Further investment in the refining sector is highly expected.

Most of India's crude oil reserves lie offshore in the western part of the country, while onshore reserves reside in the northeast. India continues to have licensing rounds. The ninth round under NELP, completed in March 2012, attracted seventy-four bids. India is in the process of constructing a strategic petroleum reserve to protect the country against potential disruptions.

India is seeing a steady increase in its natural gas production. However, current demand has exceeded supply, so at present the country remains a net importer of natural gas. India is also exploring the opportunities of unconventional gas plays, including using horizontal drilling shale gas plays. In addition, several regional liquefied natural gas and pipeline projects have been implemented or are under consideration, including the Iran-Pakistan-India Pipeline, Turkmenistan-Afghanistan-Pakistan-India Pipeline, and shipments imported from Myanmar.

Meantime, India continues to suffer from a severe shortage of electricity-generation capacity. According to the World Bank, approximately 40 percent of residences in India are without electricity. India is currently focusing a great deal of attention to nuclear power to meet these needs. In his 2010 book, *The Rough Guide to The Energy Crisis*, David Buchan reported that people in rural India are not connected to the electric grid, so must still rely on basic biofuels such as animal dung for cooking.[4] Up to 80 percent of India's population depends on firewood for cooking.

Notes for Chapter 4

1. *Wall Street Journal.* December 3, 2011.
2. *The Oklahoman.* June 11, 2011.
3. *Wall Street Journal.* December 3, 2011.
4. Buchnan, David. *Rough Guide to the Energy Crisis.* London: Rough Guides. 2010. p 4.

Please use this space to make notes about this chapter for later reference.

5

Demand on the International Front

"A people . . . who are possessed of the spirit of commerce, who see and who will pursue their advantages, may achieve almost anything."
—**President George Washington**

International players in the US energy market are dramatically increasing their investment. Energy companies from Spain, China, and France have spent billions of dollars on America's future energy plays. American oil and gas corporations including Chesapeake Energy, SandRidge Energy, and Devon Energy have sold properties to such foreign entities during the economic downturn. For example, Chesapeake sold billions of dollars' worth of assets they held in this country.

This influx of foreign investment in our natural resources is a mixed blessing. On the one hand, it provided a cash infusion for these companies. On the other hand, foreign ownership of our natural resources, especially by nations that are economically or politically unstable, could present an energy security threat in the future. Although these foreign companies are positioning their ownership here as an investment necessary to continue exploration critical to their needs, we can only hope that their stated intent continues as a mutually beneficial relationship in the future.

The Driving Impact of the Consumer

Then: In 2008 the US sat at the top of the list of consumption of oil, followed by China, Japan, Russia, Germany, and others. America comprised approximately 5 percent of the world's population, but used over 25 percent of the eighty-five million or so barrels per day of oil processed, along with a proximate percentage of cleaner, more abundant North American natural gas. The US Department of Energy estimated that over the next twenty years, US oil consumption would rise by 33 percent, natural gas consumption by 60 percent, and demand for electricity by 45 percent.

The international factor had to be figured into demand as well. World demand was not going away anytime soon unless major factors, such as the worldwide recession, persisted. The best assumptions were that once the recession ended, demand both here at home and abroad would explode.

Now: The EIA projects energy consumption in world markets will grow by 53 percent from 2008 to 2035.

Then: Back in 2008 the world's oil was coming from Saudi Arabia, Russia, the United States, Iran, China, and other countries. In Africa, problems—including kidnappings, pipeline attacks in Nigeria, civil unrest, and operational difficulties—plagued production.

Now: In early 2012 *The Oklahoman* reported that Nigeria, one of the biggest suppliers of oil to this country, could shut off the spigot due to a possible strike, pushing crude and gasoline prices higher for Americans. Nigeria supplies 8 percent of America's total oil imports, so any disruption could cause a price spike.[1]

In Asia, China's dominant energy source remains coal, but the country's transportation fuel needs could create a tremendous demand for oil. This crunch is taking shape amidst a power struggle between the US, China, Russia, and Iran. South Korea, which imports all its fossil fuels, has announced plans to become an energy producer. Large underwater deposits of gas hydrates have been discovered beneath the ocean off its coast.

In Europe the question of whether Russia would be able to increase exports remains. Reports have shown Russian oil production output falling by 1 percent in 2008 from the previous year. Russia also continues to use its natural gas resources as a political weapon by turning off its supplies to countries like Bulgaria, especially during the cold winter months.

Here in North America, the US still lacks a comprehensive energy policy, and Mexican governmental resistance to privatizing the Mexican oil industry is inhibiting continued exploration. Politicians on both sides of the aisle in Mexico have protested the Mexican president's proposal to ease limits on private participation in oil and gas production.

In South America, political tensions between the US and Venezuela continue and show no signs of abating.

Then: Global demand growth for 2008 was projected at 2.3 percent, with very little spare capacity in oil production. Many national oil companies were having difficulty maintaining current output. Investment capital for energy projects was approaching a staggering amount of money on the international front. For example, General Electric Company's Energy Financial Services unit planned to invest $5 billion through 2010 in energy and water projects in Asia, Latin America, and the Middle East. In addition to GE, there were major projects that US energy companies had ongoing in the Caspian Sea region, along with Australia, the Gulf of Mexico, and Brazil. Iraq also announced that it would offer its first bids for E&P licenses since the US-led invasion in 2003.

Now: The Middle East continues to play a vital role in supplying oil. Chart 10 shows selected oil and gas pipeline infrastructures in the Middle East.

Chart 10

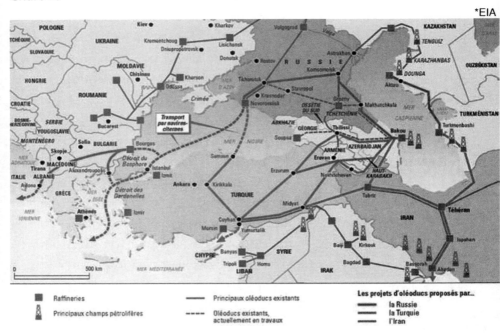

*EIA

It remains to be seen how US troop withdrawal will affect Iraq's oil production. Several companies have concerns about operating in the country once US forces have departed due to safety and security issues. Iraq's oil ministry wants to accelerate output from the present three million barrels per day to as much as twelve million barrels a day by 2017. By comparison, Saudi Arabia produces about ten million barrels a day.[2]

As you can see from Chart 11, close to half of the top world oil producers in 2010 comprised countries that are not stable economically or are facing internal political struggles. Therefore, the potential for disruptions of oil production and delivery come into play.

Chart 11

Top World Oil Producers, 2010		
(thousand barrels per day)		
Rank	Country	Production
1	Saudi Arabia	10,521
2	Russia	10,146
3	United States	9,688
4	China	4,273
5	Iran	3,252
6	Canada	3,483
7	Mexico	2,983
8	United Arab Emirates	2,813
9	Brazil	2,719
10	Nigeria	2,458
11	Kuwait	2,450
12	Iraq	2,408
13	Venezuela	2,375
14	Norway	2,134
15	Algeria	2,078

EIA 2010

On the import side of the equation, Chart 12 lists the US at the top of the national rankings of oil importers in the world.

Chart 12

Top World Oil Net Importers, 2010		
(thousand barrels per day)		
Rank	Country	Imports
1	United States	9,631
2	China	4,542
3	Japan	4,261
4	Germany	2,319
5	India	2,172
6	Korea, South	2,142
7	France	1,791
8	United Kingdom	1,566
9	Spain	1,440
10	Italy	1,397
11	Netherlands	962
12	Singapore	942
13	Taiwan	894
14	Turkey	650
15	Belgium	619

EIA 2010

The percentage of world demand by importers is about 50 percent.

Global Perspective on Cap and Trade

A heated debate over proposed legislation for a "cap and trade" system occurred in 2009. As the *Wall Street Journal* explained, although the concept behind the cap and trade system seems simple, the devil is in the details. Basically the federal government would create a market for carbon emissions, with emitters having to purchase emission allowances.

Chart 13

Cap and Trade Program
(Source: EIA)

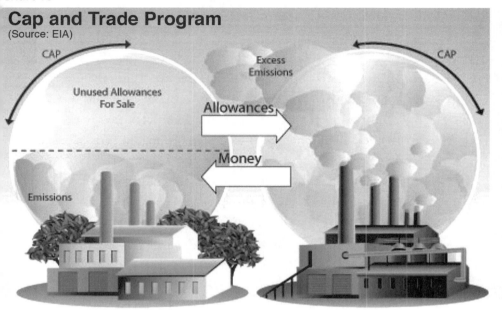

In theory this buyer and seller market would encourage companies to become more efficient in preventing carbon emissions. In reality, cap and trade would slowly put producers and users of coal, natural gas, and crude oil out of business.[3]

History is also demonstrating that this system, implemented several years ago in the European Union, doesn't achieve its stated goal. In 2008 the latest data showed that despite the cap and trade program in effect there, greenhouse-gas emissions had actually risen. Some experts felt this struggle in Europe showed how difficult it would be for the industrialized world to reduce emissions.

Already, some people have become multimillionaires by selling the credits that fund projects. Over nine billion of such credits were traded in 2007 alone. But the United Nations was questioning whether the system would ultimately succeed. For instance, in the San Francisco Bay area, hundreds of businesses would end up being charged for emissions of heat-trapping gases.

During the 2008 presidential contest in this country, the coal industry, which provides approximately half of all US electricity, was facing strong criticism from city halls to the US Capitol. All three presidential candidates distanced themselves from the coal industry as the campaign heated up. However, during one Pennsylvania visit, Barack Obama stated, "We are the Saudi Arabia of coal, and it could be a very important way for us to meet our long-term energy needs."[4] America enjoyed an abundance of coal reserves, making coal the least costly and most abundant energy resource available in the US.

FutureGen, a $1 billion-plus government-industry project, was proposed to make the most of this plentiful fossil fuel. Essentially the goal was to provide a first-of-its-kind clean power plant, with a target completion date of 2012. Nearly every facet of the prototype plant was to be based on cutting-edge technology that already existed. The goal was for this highly energy-efficient, coal-supplied power plant to produce near zero emissions. But the FutureGen project was withdrawn under the Bush administration. Then, according to the US Department of Energy, in August 2010 US Energy Secretary Steven Chu announced the awarding of $1 billion in Recovery Act funding to the FutureGen Alliance, Ameren Energy Resources, Babcock & Wilcox, and Air Liquide Process & Construction, Inc. to build FutureGen 2.0, a clean coal repowering program and carbon dioxide storage network.

The project partners plan to repower Ameren's two-hundred-megawatt Unit 4 in Meredosia, Illinois, with advance oxy-combustion technology to capture approximately 1.3 million metric tons of CO_2 each year—more than 90 percent of the plant's carbon emissions. Other emissions will be reduced to near zero levels. The mission of FutureGen Alliance will help design the test program for the new facility to incorporate a broad range of coals and operating conditions to expand the market for this repowering approach.

Although FutureGen appeared to be on hold as of early 2012, Chu remains committed to the FutureGen project as an American energy solution. According to the US Department of Energy, Chu stated, "This investment in the world's first commercial-scale oxy-combustion power plant will help to open up the over $300 billion market for coal unit repowering and position the country as a leader in an important part of the global clean energy economy."

Going Forward Globally

Despite all the concerns related to the moving parts of the energy industry, there is good reason to be optimistic. Right now we are seeing a shale play throughout the country, as well as the oil play in the Bakken. For the first time in many years we are drilling more oil than natural gas. At the same time, we have not yet achieved that true balance in terms of energy sources that can lead us to total independence. And even if we should reach that point, it would not take too much to quickly get us out of balance and fall back on our reliance on imported oil.

For now we are dependent on foreign oil, but we don't want to be complacent. That is where you, the American consumer, must step up and decide. Some may say they see the point here, but they don't care because they prefer our current sources of energy. Others may agree that we need to balance our energy needs with environmental preservation, so it is necessary to look at natural gas or some other alternative. The big question will be if consumers are willing to pay more—maybe a tremendous amount more—to get off oil for good. That is where you, the consumer, will be driving our energy policy, helping to create the People's Energy Plan.

This first section of the book has given you the background information you need to understand the variables of the energy equation. Next we will look at the alternative forms of energy available, along with their pros and cons.

Notes for Chapter 5

1. *The Oklahoman.* January 14, 2012.
2. *Wall Street Journal.* December 24, 2011.
3. *Wall Street Journal.* April 4, 2008.
4. *CNN.* September 14, 2008.

Please use this space to make notes about this chapter
for later reference.

Part II

Energy Sources: Here and Now

6

Our Energy Future: Options Available in America

"The elements of our strengths are many. They include our democratic government, our economic system, our great natural resources."

—Ambassador Jeane Kirkpatrick

When Peter Voser took charge of Royal Dutch Shell as CEO in 2009, he set a goal to make Shell the most competitive and innovative energy company in the world, despite the fact that current economic factors placed considerable obstacles in the way of his goal of implementing a new energy blueprint. In a speech he gave in London in 2010 he said, "Shell and its competitors faced the unprecedented challenge of building a more sustainable energy system while responding to the worst economic downturn since the 1930s."[1] Yet by the end of 2011, for the first time fuel was the number one US export based on dollars, with our country shipping more gasoline, diesel, and jet fuel than any other export.[2]

Today, America is blessed with an abundance of traditional natural resources, including oil, gas, and coal, which can be explored and developed to help meet our energy needs. In addition, we possess a constellation of alternative options, including renewables, which can be added into the mix to achieve our goal of total energy independence. Chart 14 illustrates US energy consumption in 2010 by these various sources to give you an idea of where we currently stand.

Chart 14

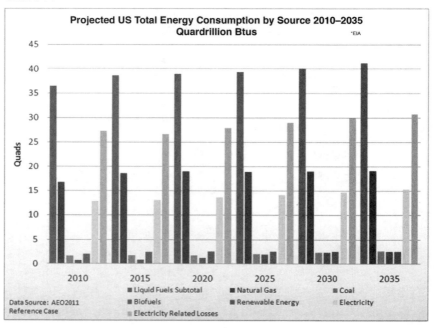

In this chapter, we look at each of these sources more in depth, along with their pros and cons.

Oil

Men and women have greatly sacrificed over the years so that we could have energy to drive our cars, watch television, listen to the radio, and provide us energy security. In *The Secret of Sherwood Forest*, authors Guy H. Woodward and Grace Steele Woodward reveal how during World War II, oilmen fought the war by following the drill bit, pipeline, test tube, and refinery plants wherever they led throughout the world:

Some fought the war in the frozen North at the Arctic Circle, others in the steaming, insect-infested jungles of the tropics. Others flew the hump over the Himalayas with fuel for our Chinese allies. Some spent their days and nights in the laboratories with their crucibles and test tubes. Many served their seven-day weeks as governmental aides in performing the many administrative duties demanded by total war. Thanks to a farseeing and wise nation that had refused to burden its oil industry with crushing controls by rigid laws, rules, and regulations, but had on the contrary, encouraged the men engaged in the hazardous business of finding and producing oil. Because of this policy, followed by more than twenty-five years, the United States reserves were sufficient to sustain a growing, healthy economy in time of peace and now furnished security and the ingredients of victory in time of war.[3]

Today, men and women continue to sacrifice for our energy needs, even though we have not had a strategic energy plan in place for sixty years. Fortunately, the increase in potential oil reserves in the US has risen dramatically over the last few years, and in 2012 America is expected to export a significant amount of diesel and gasoline refined from crude. In addition, by 2013 this country could begin exporting chilled natural gas.[4]

The increase in our oil reserves is primarily due to the Bakken Play in North Dakota. During the winter, the cold climate in the Bakken makes it a difficult place to live. Yet men and women working there are committed to a strong energy future for America. Energy companies in the Bakken and other places around the country are trying to survive, but they are now burdened with rigid laws, rules, and regulations. Although reasonable regulations are welcome in the energy industry, burdensome regulations are very costly to business and consumers in our country. We must consider the ultimate impact of the Endangered Species Act, Clean Air Act Amendments, and other environmental regulations on the production, refining, and distribution of crude oil and petroleum products. Overall, the energy industry has a remarkable track record of striving for energy efficiency and environmental preservation. But too much regulation is endangering America's prosperity and security.

As of 2012, the oil rig count in the US has surpassed the natural gas rig count, approximately 1,200 oil rigs to 800 natural gas rigs. To put this in perspective, back in 1981 the total oil and gas rig count in the US reached 4,530, then fell to a low of 488 in 1999. That means today we have only 2,000 rigs compared to 4,530 rigs twenty years ago, and it dropped as low as 480 working rigs a decade or so ago.[5] Rig counts are mostly a function of supply and demand. Due to the recent discoveries of oil in the Bakken Play and natural gas shale plays nationwide, we are seeing a flip flop in the count. We presently find ourselves with an abundance of natural gas and oil in this country, but with a current oversupply of natural gas, it makes more economic sense to drill for oil at $100 a barrel, and not for natural gas.

When it comes to oil, the number one question in the mind of most consumers is why gasoline prices seem so high. However, as previously shown, when compared to other popular commodities, gas prices do not appear that costly. As Kenneth P. Green of the American Enterprise Institute for Public Policy Research explains, three key factors drive the price of gas at the pump:

1. Higher gas prices induce consumers to tighten their belts and politicians to call for taxes on oil companies, which in turn get passed back to consumers, driving prices upward.
2. About 85 percent of oil price hikes are due to supply and demand of petroleum, not the whim of oil companies.
3. The remaining 15 percent of oil price hikes is likely attributable to environment-conscious regulations.

To help lower gas prices and promote domestic employment and trade benefits in the future, policymakers should facilitate drilling offshore and in Arctic National Wildlife Refuge and offshore drilling, as well as lift boutique-fuel requirements for fuel additives. The Federal Clean Air Act established national fuel emission standards that allow states to adopt unique fuel programs to meet local air quality needs, and twelve states have adopted their own clean fuel programs for part or all of the state. Most of these programs set lower gasoline volatility requirements than federal standards, and most are effective for only part of the year. In addition, marginal wells are very important to America. The average production nationally of active marginal wells is 2.18 barrels of oil per day and 15.5 thousand cubic feet (mcf) per day for gas wells. Marginal wells make billions of dollars of economic impact nationally each year.[6]

Today, oil provides more than 96 percent of the fuel for the US transportation fleet, and at least 69 percent of our oil is used by the transportation sector.[7] Despite the recent increase in our oil reserves, America remains heavily dependent on crude oil imports. From January 2011 to October 2011, America was the world's largest importer of crude oil, taking in 2.7 billion barrels of oil worth roughly $280 billion.[8] In 2010 the US imported approximately 11.8 million barrels of petroleum per day, which accounted for almost half of the petroleum consumed in the country.

The average American consumer has no idea of the immense number of items they use that are petroleum-based products, including CD players, dentures, insect repellant, and running shoes, to name but a few (a complete list is to be found in the appendix). To transport oil to the manufacturers of these products, as well as heating oil companies and gas stations, requires a huge infrastructure. As *Forbes* notes, "The United States built its first pipeline in the 1840s, and there are now more than a million kilometers of oil and gas pipelines."[9] Lack of an energy plan, however, has left at least half of these pipelines, some of which are half a century old, badly in need of updating.

The antiquated state of this infrastructure is one important reason why the proposed Keystone XL Pipeline project is so critical to our energy security. "Resistance to the completion of Canada's Keystone XL pipeline could deny US consumers access to a voluminous supply of oil and the jobs that would attend its creation and operation," asserted Kenneth P. Green of the American Enterprise Institute. The refusal in January 2012 by the Obama administration to permit the Keystone XL project to go forward has forced Canadian leaders into working actively on another option, a proposed pipeline that would ship crude from Canada's oil sands areas of development to the Pacific.[10]

Another key issue our energy plan needs to address is whether America needs to expand its Strategic Oil Reserve.

Oil Pros:
- Oil has high heating value.
- Gasoline and petroleum products are easily accessible by consumers.
- Oil is used in thousands of everyday products.
- Oil is easily distributed.

Oil Cons:
- Burning oil releases extra carbon dioxide.
- Oil carries geopolitical risk to its supply and demand.
- Oil is now harder to find, thus more expensive.
- Used oil is difficult to clean and recycle.

Natural Gas

Natural gas is an energy answer that is available today. We should definitely be putting it to use now. For years I have voiced my belief that natural gas reserves are critical to a strong US economy and extremely important for America's energy security. Natural gas is an abundant, clean fuel that has many domestic uses—from heating our homes to serving as an alternative to gasoline. It is the bridge fuel to our country's energy sustainability.

Natural gas exploration today is a growing part of the global energy mix. The EIA recently reported that there are forty-eight gas shale basins outside the US and almost seventy gas shale formations in thirty-two countries. Canada, Mexico, Chile, Australia, Algeria, and Brazil currently produce substantial amounts of natural gas.

Over the last few years shale gas has become a major topic of discussion in the media for several reasons. Until recent years, natural gas was primarily produced from "conventional" reservoirs via vertical technology. "Unconventional" natural gas production includes hydraulic fracturing and horizontal drilling to extract supplies from tight sand formations and shale formations where natural gas is trapped. Due to technological advancements, shale formations have been discovered in numerous basins not only in America but around the world. In fact, there has been such success in these finds that there is currently a natural gas supply bubble. In America, energy companies have identified a one-hundred-year supply of natural gas.

These finds have prompted public questions and concerns about the process of extracting natural gas. Hydraulic fracturing, in particular, is raising concerns for the safety of environment. However, consumers need to know that the hydraulic fracturing process, or "fracking" as it is more commonly known, has been in use for more than sixty years. Once the drilling of a well has been completed, the shale is cracked by tiny ruptures, allowing the application of water, sand, and a small amount of chemical additives to release natural gas. There have been minimal reports of improper disposal of wastewater, but energy companies involved in fracking realize the importance of water resources for generations ahead, so they are applying technology to clean and reuse water. Many companies even post information about the fracking fluids they are using.

Recently, US Senator Jim Inhofe of Oklahoma, a ranking member of the Senate Environment and Public Works Committee, took issue with a draft analysis issued by the EPA in December 2011 indicating that compounds likely linked with hydraulic fracturing and natural gas production are in ground water and drinking wells in a Wyoming community. "EPA's conclusions are not based on sound science but rather on political science," Inhofe said. "Its findings are premature, given that the agency has not gone through the necessary peer-review process, and there are still serious outstanding questions regarding EPA's data and methodology." According to Inhofe, the fracking process was first used in Oklahoma in 1948. "There's not been a documented case of ground water contamination," he noted, making it clear he views EPA's draft analysis as just the latest move by the Obama administration in what he sees as its war against fossil fuels and affordable energy.

Another issue being raised is whether earthquakes are associated with hydraulic fracking. A few months ago I experienced three earthquakes in Oklahoma—the largest was a 5.7 magnitude. The year before, however, I had lived through my first earthquake while in Japan—a 6.3 magnitude. As to the reason for the earthquakes, I can only say that I have lived in the center of oil and gas activity for most of my life, and that was the first time I ever experienced an earthquake there, so I find it interesting that this is only the first time that I would have been in an earthquake in Oklahoma if it were due to hydraulic fracking. According to the US Geological Survey, an earthquake of a magnitude 5.6 similar to the earthquake in Oklahoma on November 5, 2011, is believed to be capable of striking anywhere in eastern North America at irregular intervals. The Oklahoma Geological Survey also noted the earthquakes were centered more than three miles below the ground, far below drilling in the area. To date, both the US Geological Survey and Oklahoma Geological Survey have found no definitive link to seismic activity and natural gas activity.

My personal experience notwithstanding, the debate over fracking and seismic activity has begun. According to *USA Today*, Art McGarr of the US Geological Survey office has asserted that since an incident outside Denver in the 1960s, geologists have known that deep injections of wastewater, placed in the ground to avoid cleanup costs, can trigger earthquakes.[11] Note, however, that he was not talking about fracking, but about wastewater wells. Disposing of wastewater can be better served by sending the wastewater to treatment plants, for example. Meantime, Ohio is another state (in addition to New York) that has halted drilling in the Youngstown area to review data about injection wells and the correlation to earthquakes that have taken place in that area.[12]

Another question being asked is how natural gas emissions compare to oil or coal. The answer is that when natural gas is used to generate electricity, natural gas emits half the CO_2 of coal and 80 percent less than nitrogen oxides. From a transportation standpoint, CNG vehicles emit 25 percent less CO_2 than vehicles that run on traditional gasoline or diesel. This holds great promise for the future of CNG for our transportation needs. First used as transportation fuel during World War II, CNG currently powers more than ten million vehicles on the road worldwide, including over 100,000 vehicles in the US. Costs for CNG are, on average, 40 percent lower than gasoline. At present, though, there are hurdles for consumers interested in converting a vehicle to CNG, and purchasing a CNG vehicle is more costly, but a strong case can be made that investment in a CNG vehicle will be recouped over a short period of time due to the price differential between CNG and gasoline. Another problem at present is the lack of available infrastructure in this country. Chesapeake Energy is taking a lead with the formation of $1 billion venture capital fund for investment and technologies to support CNG infrastructure nationally, which will greatly advance CNG as a transportation fuel.

Natural gas also holds promise for power generation. About 22 percent of electric-generating capacity in America is currently natural gas–fired. According to the EIA, natural gas usage rates for electricity generation grew 38 percent from 2001 to 2010. Natural gas power plants are also less costly to build. Until the recent success of shale plays around this country, Russia, Iran, and Qatar had owned more than half of the world's natural gas reserves. Given the enormous finds here, we should establish a more efficient, accessible natural gas transportation and distribution system.

"Everyone seems fond of comparisons with Saudi Arabia when it comes to energy, but few realize that the US is the Saudi Arabia of natural gas, with production greater than Russia and a two-hundred-year supply that exceeds the equivalent of oil reserves of Saudi Arabia," reports David Sweet, executive director of the World Alliance for Decentralized Energy. According to him, the natural gas industry directly employs 622,000 people and indirectly sustains an additional 2.2 million jobs.[13]

Bob Tippee, editor of *Oil and Gas Journal*, noted at an IEPC roundtable in November 2011:

> Always a ravenous importer of oil, the United States was supposed to import a growing amount of methane in the form of LNG. Then—surprise!—the country became able to produce all the natural gas it needs—and more. The gas . . . occurs in low-permeability rock strata—especially shales—that hadn't produced much before. Until very recently, no one knew how to make it happen. Now companies are drilling horizontal wells and, in effect, manufacturing the permeability that nature didn't provide with hydraulic fracturing. Suddenly, huge new volumes of natural gas have appeared in pipelines and—more importantly—on the development horizon.

Development of coal bed methane is another energy source vital to our country. Coal bed methane, or CBM, is a form of natural gas extracted from coal beds. CBM is distinct from a typical sandstone or other conventional gas reservoir, as the methane is stored within the coal by a process called adsorption. CBM contains very little heavier hydrocarbons such as propane or butane, and no natural gas condensate. It often contains up to a few percent of carbon dioxide.

NGV Inc.: My Personal CNG Story

In 1992 I went into the CNG–NGV business when very few others were interested, even though Boone Pickens was rallying everyone to convert their vehicles to CNG. I named my company NGV, Inc. At that time, most gasoline stations had no interest in carrying CNG. Only a few locally owned stations saw the future need. However, United Parcel Service was one company that did take the lead at that time, and they remain in the forefront to this day. As Portia Crump stated in a 1995 issue of *CNG Update*, "They may not have the sleek lines of Detroit's newest concept cars, but UPS vehicles are on the cutting edge of today's hottest technology."

The year before, in 1994, UPS Automotive Manager David Tripoli—who received a State Industry Award by Charles Nesbitt, Oklahoma's Secretary of Energy—acknowledged (at the third annual International Energy Policy Conference that I had founded), "United Parcel Service shares the nation's growing concern about urban air quality as well as the dependency on petroleum-based foreign fuel." At that time, UPS was operating 142 vehicles on Oklahoma City and Tulsa streets and roadways. At the conference, UPS announced plans to expand its fleet with projects in Connecticut and Georgia.

Oklahoma had passed legislation in 1991—the first of its kind in the nation—to make it economically possible for private fleet operators to build the necessary associated CNG infrastructure, including fueling stations and fuel yard facilities. During 1992 and 1993, I spoke to several civic groups about the importance of NGV and CNG to our energy future, assuring them that the natural gas industry had a great opportunity to promote economic and environmental stability for our nation. "It is imperative that the purchase of CNG vehicles, conversion of vehicles, and the construction of refueling stations for the use of CNG be encouraged within the state of Oklahoma," I advised. I converted my company car to a duel usage of CNG and gasoline, and emblazoned the car with our company tagline: "NGV Inc., Natural Gas Vehicles: America's Energy Future."

Two decades later I have to wonder where America would be if we would have adopted and embraced the CNG technology that my company NGV was advocating. Certainly our dependence on foreign oil would have been diminished. We'd be more dependent on natural gas, and the abundant supply of natural gas in our own country today would be used. We would also be using a cleaner fuel, so in every way we would be far ahead of where we are today from an energy standpoint, and closer to energy independence that we could have imagined.

Natural Gas Pros:

- Natural gas burns more cleanly than other fossil fuels.
- Natural gas can be piped into homes to provide heating, cooking, and to run appliances.
- Natural gas can be used as a fuel for vehicles.
- Natural gas is relatively abundant, clean-burning, and easy to distribute.

Natural Gas Cons:

- America currently lacks a national infrastructure for CNG use.
- Converting vehicles to CNG is costly.
- Though cleaner than oil or coal, natural gas still contributes carbon dioxide.

The GET

The documentary film *The Grand Energy Transition* (*The GET*), released in 2012, is based on the book of the same name by Robert A. Hefner III, founder and owner of GHK Exploration, who pioneered deep and ultra-deep natural gas exploration. In the book, which Ted Turner deemed important enough to buy for members of Congress and Fortune CEOs, Hefner forecasts the continuing decline of coal and oil, and predicts the coming "age of energy gases."[14] America's abundant natural gas will serve as the major bridge to this new energy age, along with wind and solar power, to create a new, hydrogen-based economy.

Hefner addresses President Obama in his book, suggesting that America convert at least half of our vehicle fleet to CNG by 2020. In Hefner's opinion, this conversion would reduce our oil imports by over five million barrels per day and save Americans tens of trillions of dollars in payments to foreign oil producers over the coming decades. Hefner also believes the expanded use of natural gas would provide America with jobs, prosperity, and greater national security.

Coal

Since a quarter of the world's coal reserves are located in the US, it has long been considered a major natural resource for America's energy future. Coal is currently mined in twenty-six states with Wyoming, West Virginia, Kentucky, and Montana leading in coal production. Most of the coal in the US is mined for the use of generating electricity, and it provides over half of this country's electricity generation power. In 2007 coal accounted for 27 percent of world energy consumption. We have enough coal in the US to last 249 years.

Canada is the largest importer of US coal. Outside of this country, the two top deposits of coal are located in Russia and China. It is currently projected that world coal consumption will increase by 56 percent from 2007 to 2035, with US coal consumption during that same time frame expected to increase by a little over 1 percent.

The opposition to coal, however, is that it is not a viable option because of the environmental pollution it produces. Due to the enormous pressure to clean up this pollution, the US government has stepped in to develop technologies for emission-free coal plants that will capture CO_2 so that it does not enter the atmosphere.

"The Environmental Protection Agency wants to force utilities to install expensive pollution scrubbers at coal-fired power plants. AEP-PSO said it would have to shut down a coal plant in Oologah [Oklahoma] for up to two years while scrubbers are installed," reported *The Oklahoman* in June 2011, noting that costs are in the billions and will be passed on to consumers and customers.[15] According to the US Department of Commerce, for the US to maintain its competiveness and at the same time meet environmental, health, and safety requirements, we will need to accelerate international transfer of new coal-related technologies.

It is interesting to note that synthetic fuel, a.k.a. synfuel, is a liquid fuel obtained from coal (also from natural gas, oil shale, or biomass). It may also refer to fuels derived from other solids such as plastics or rubber waste. The process of creating synfuels is known as Fischer Tropsch conversion, a methanol to gasoline conversion or direct liquefaction. The Fischer Tropsch process was first used in World War II. In fact, the process was developed in Germany in 1923.

Coal Pros:
- The US has over a two-hundred-year supply of coal.
- Coal can be transformed into liquid or gas for transportation.
- A large amount of electricity can be produced using coal at a low price.
- Coal is relatively cheap in comparison to other energy alternatives.

Coal Cons:
- Transforming coal to a liquid is a very expensive process.
- CO_2 sequestration is needed.
- Coal burning produces a large amount of pollution, acid rain, and carbon dioxide.

Hydroelectric

Most federal hydroelectric (hydropower) projects are constructed and operated by either the US Army Corps of Engineers or the Department of Interior's Bureau of Reclamation. Electric power from hydroelectric projects is marketed by the federal government's power marketing administrations (Bonneville, Southwestern, Southeastern, Western Area, and Alaska). Most non-federal hydroelectric projects are regulated and licensed by the Federal Energy Regulatory Commission.[16]

At present, hydroelectric plants contribute about 7 percent of total electric power generated in this country. Water flowing through the dams spins turbine blades that are connected to generators. The power produced is sent to homes and businesses. Most hydroelectric power plants have a dam and a reservoir because the process utilizes a large quantity of water. The EIA reports that China is currently the largest producer of hydroelectricity, followed by Canada, Brazil, and the US.

Hydroelectric Pros:
- Hydroelectric is the most widely used form of renewable energy.
- Hydroelectric is independent of fossil fuels.
- The operational costs involved in hydroelectric are low.

Hydroelectric Cons:
- Hydroelectric power generation requires a large reservoir.
- The location of hydroelectric power can be a challenge because of the area needed to construct a huge reservoir.
- Droughts can impact hydroelectric power generation.

Notes for Chapter 6

1. London Business School Global Leadership Summit. May 7, 2010. *New Energy for a Changing World.*
2. *The Oklahoman.* December 31, 2011.
3. Woodward, Guy H., and Woodward, Grace Steele. Preface to *The Secret of Sherwood Forest.* Norman, Oklahoma: University of Oklahoma Press. 2002.
4. *Wall Street Journal.* January 3, 2012.
5. *The Journal Record.* December 30, 2011.
6. Oklahoma Marginal Well Commission.
7. Sandalow, David. *Freedom from Oil.* New York: McGraw-Hill. 2007. p. 2.

8. *The Oklahoman.* December 31, 2011.
9. *Forbes.* December 29, 2011.
10. *Wall Street Journal.* January 9, 2012.
11. *USA Today.* January 4, 2012.
12. *Wall Street Journal.* January 3, 2012.
13. Sweet, David M. "An Energy Upgrade for the US." *The Washington Times.* September 28, 2011.
14. Hefner, Robert A. III. *The Grand Energy Transition.* New Jersey: Wiley. 2009.
15. *The Oklahoman.* June 18, 2011.
16. US Department of Commerce.

Please use this space to make notes about this chapter
for later reference.

7

Our Energy Future II:
More Options Available in America

"Independence is the recognition of the fact that yours is the responsibility of judgment and nothing can help you escape it—that no substitute can do your thinking, as no pinch-hitter can live your life."

—**Ayn Rand**

Hydrogen

Hydrogen can be extracted from the ocean by running an electric current through the water, but this process—known as electrolysis—requires enormous quantities of electricity. According to the Hydrogen Energy Center, four realities suggest that the current energy economy is not sustainable:

1. The demand for energy is growing and the raw materials for the fossil fuel economy are diminishing. Oil, coal, and natural gas supplies are not replenished as they are consumed, so an alternative must be found.

2. Most of the people who consume fossil fuels don't live where fuels are extracted.

3. Emissions from fossil fuel usage significantly degrade air quality all over the world.

4. Third-world economies are especially susceptible when developing energy systems needed to improve their economies.

Hydrogen has three basic benefits that address these concerns:
1. The use of hydrogen greatly reduces pollution. When hydrogen is combined with oxygen in a fuel cell, energy in the form of electricity is produced. This electricity can be used to power vehicles, or as a heat source, or applied to other uses.
2. Hydrogen can be produced locally from numerous sources. Hydrogen can be produced either centrally and then distributed or onsite where it will be used. Hydrogen gas can be produced from methane (natural gas), gasoline, biomass, coal, or water.
3. If hydrogen is produced from water, we have a sustainable production system. Electrolysis is the method of separating water into hydrogen and oxygen. Renewable energy can be used to power electrolyzers to produce the hydrogen from water. Some of the renewable sources used to power electrolyzers are wind, hydro, solar, and tidal energy.

The Energy Policy Act of 2005 authorized more than $2 billion for a hydrogen fuel cell program by 2020, along with loan guarantees for nuclear power plants, clean coal technology, and wind energy. Hydrogen today is used to power commercial buses, and hydrogen is used in many commercial applications from welding metal, to dying fabrics, to making electronic plastics and fertilizers.

It should be noted that renewable energy sources are often limited for commercial use due to their intermittent availability. Sometimes the wind doesn't blow and the sun doesn't shine, and when that happens, hydrogen could be a critical link used as a storage medium to supply the needed power during these periods. It is also critical to realize that natural gas equals CH_4 (methane), which means natural gas will be an important factor when we enter the hydrogen economy.

Hydrogen Pros:

- Hydrogen burns cleanly.
- Hydrogen can be quickly refueled.
- Hydrogen is the most abundant element on the planet.
- Hydrogen is twice as efficient as gasoline.

Hydrogen Cons:

- A large quantity of energy is required to produce hydrogen for energy.
- There is no hydrogen infrastructure.
- Few refueling stations for hydrogen-powered cars exist.

Geothermal

Geothermal energy emanates from the natural heat of the earth. Using steam from the geothermal reservoir coming from wells, heat is routed to generators to produce electricity. Also, generating plants use water at temperatures greater than 360°F, pumping it under high pressure to generation equipment at the surface. The heat from geothermal energy can be used directly for heating and air conditioning units, as well as to heat water.

The US has geothermal plants, which are mainly located in Nevada and California. At present, California exceeds all states in geothermal usage, but such energy can be tapped in most locations with the use of geothermal heat pumps. The current cost for usage is approximately 5¢ per kilowatt. Great potential for the use of geothermal energy exists nationwide and worldwide. Over 150 power plants are under development in more than a dozen states, which will triple geothermal generating capacity in the US.

Geothermal Pros:

- Direct use of geothermal energy is available for consumer applications.
- Geothermal energy is clean, with low emissions.

- Geothermal energy is available around the clock.
- Geothermal energy is domestically based.
- Geothermal energy is a renewable source.

Geothermal Cons:
- Installation of geothermal energy plans requires wide spaces and long pipes.
- Therefore, areas of dense population can experience longer times to get energy.

Nuclear Fission

The first US nuclear power plant went into commercial production in 1957 at Shippingport, Pennsylvania. At present, 104 reactors are in operation in this country at present. According to the World Nuclear Association, in 2009 there were 436 reactors in thirty countries around the globe, with 52 more under construction and another 135 planned. Due to the Fukushima nuclear power plant disaster in Japan, however, the entire nuclear energy sector is facing uncertainty. Primary issues to be resolved include the status of advanced design nuclear power plants, fairness of the licensing process by the Nuclear Regulatory Commission (NRC), and status of a permanent nuclear waste repository.

Nuclear Fission Pros:
- Nuclear fission is emission-free.
- Nuclear fission enables 24–7 operations.
- Nuclear fission is a less expensive alternative for the consumer.

Nuclear Fission Cons:
- Regulatory constraints on nuclear plans are stringent.
- Nuclear fission produces radioactive waste.

Nuclear Fusion

An international project is underway to build a nuclear-fusion reactor, known as the International Thermonuclear Experimental Reactor (ITER), at an estimated cost of $12 billion. This reactor would demonstrate that power can be generated using the energy released when two light atomic nuclei are brought together to make a heavier one—a process similar to the one that powers the sun. Scientists working in this sector claim that within thirty years nuclear fusion will become available for commercial use.

Nuclear Fusion Pros:
- The products of a fusion reaction are not radioactive, so there is no nuclear waste.
- There is no threat of meltdowns in a nuclear fusion reactor.
- The fuels produced by fusion that could be used are relatively inexpensive and readily available.

Nuclear Fusion Cons:
- The ignition temperature of nuclear fusion is extremely high.
- Large-scale fusion reactions are very expensive.

Biomass

Biomass is plant matter used to create energy. For example, ethanol is a fuel that can be made from plants such as switch grass, and at one time was seen by the government as a solution to reducing America's dependence on foreign oil. "E10," a blend of 90 percent gasoline and 10 percent ethanol, is in use throughout the US.[1] Most cars can run on E10. "E85," a blend of 85 percent ethanol and 15 percent gasoline, known as "flex fuel," can power some automobile engines as well.[2]

Only a few years ago the number of ethanol facilities under construction was on the rise. As reported by *Popular Mechanics*, "East Kansas Agri-Energy's Ethanol facility [is] one of 100 or so such heartland garrisons in America's slowly gathering battle to reduce its dependence on fossil fuels."[3] But by 2011 US ethanol producers were faced with slowing growth in demand and turning to a fledging market for corn oil to help boost their revenues.

Biomass Pros:
- Ethanol can be used to make a variety of fuels to generate electricity.
- Ethanol can be used for the production of chemical products.
- Ethanol is an abundant natural resource.

Biomass Cons:
- Biocrops have a higher value than food; therefore they can detract from food production, leading to food shortages and increased prices for food.
- Many pollutants are released into the atmosphere in the production of ethanol.
- Ethanol fuels have been heavily subsidized by the US government.

Solar

"In the beginning the earth was without form, and void, with darkness upon the face of the deep, And God said, let there be light, and there was light, and He divided light from darkness, and day from night, and the evening and the morning were the first day."

—Genesis 1:1-5

Without the sun, life could not exist on earth. Plants use the sun's light to make food, and hundreds of millions of years ago, decaying plants produced the coal, oil, and natural gas that we use today. Solar energy uses technology to capture the power from the sun's rays.[5] At present, the Delaware Nation in Oklahoma is constructing a 37.5

kilowatt solar array on the roof of its complex that is expected to supply 30 percent of power for the buildings.[6] Chevron Corporation is also relying on steam generated by solar panels in its oil field in Coalinga, California, to heat crude oil.[7] Photovoltaic (PV) cells, concentrating solar power technologies and solar-heated water, are other solar technologies being developed by the Department of Energy. PV cells are used for everything from powering watches to the electric grid.[8]

Solar Pros:
- Solar energy is secure.
- Solar energy is normally reliable in certain areas of the country.
- Solar energy is clean.

Solar Cons:
- Solar energy can be costly to produce.
- Solar energy is largely financed by government incentives.

Wind

The EIA reports that worldwide wind power generation exceeded 200 billion kilowatt hours in 2008, which was equivalent to the annual electricity consumption of over 18 million average households in the US. One 1.5 megawatt (MW) wind turbine can produce electricity for about 400 homes annually. Denmark gets 20 percent of its energy from wind. At this time, Germany has more wind turbines than any other country. Currently, the US produces about 1 percent of our electricity from wind. In 2010 China passed the US in newly installed and total wind power capacity.

Currently, Texas leads in newly installed wind power capacity, followed by Illinois, California, South Dakota, and Minnesota.[9] In order to launch wind energy in Oklahoma, the Oklahoma Department of Commerce funded the Oklahoma Wind Power Initiative, which conducted a study to develop a resource map using information from a network of weather stations in the state. With the use of the network's high-resolution data, and terrain and geographical data, this study assisted companies—and attracted investors—in properly assessing the value of Oklahoma's wind resources. But the Osage Nation is currently opposing companies proposing to build wind farms in Osage County, Oklahoma, arguing that such farms could interfere with the extraction of oil and gas in the county.[10]

According to the *Oklahoma Gazette* in 2011, one couple in Oklahoma is living a life of energy sustainability. Bruce Johnson and Barbara Hagen grow much of their own food, generate their own electricity, provide their own heating, pump and purify their own water, and use as little fossil fuel and externally generated energy as possible. Their energy sources are solar and wind.[11]

Wind Pros:
- Wind is inexpensive.
- Wind is clean and produces no pollution.
- Presently, wind power costs are between three to five cents per kilowatt hour.
- Wind can revitalize rural economies.

Wind Cons:
- Wind turbines alter the scenic view.
- Wind turbines can be loud.
- Wind turbines kill birds.
- America is far behind the rest of the world in wind energy usage.

Nanotechnology

A potentially bright future exists for nanotechnology and the energy industry. According to the Baker Institute Energy Forum at Rice University, breakthroughs in nanotechnology hold the possibility of going beyond current sources of energy supply, particularly through technologies that can introduce materials more efficient, inexpensive, environmentally safe, and stronger and lighter than steel. For example, nanotubing and other nano-based materials could transport electricity over longer distances at increased efficiencies.

The hope is that nanotechnology may also offer a revolutionary means of widespread collection, conversion, and transmission of solar energy to render it more affordable. Another possibility is its use in batteries. "Nanotechnology may revolutionize batteries in the next few years," reports *Freedom from Oil*. "Nano processes can be used to make electrodes with much larger surface areas, for example, dramatically improving battery performance."[12]

At present, most nanotechnology research is being conducted by the private sector, but the US government should adopt an energy policy to encourage research and development into this promising scientific process that could boost our energy resources at home.

Auto Efficiency and the Demand

Competition is well under way to provide efficient vehicles for the US, as well as the world.

Plug-in or electric cars, hybrids or flex-fuel cars, and CNG cars today include the Prius, Chevy Volt, BYD F3DM, Aptera 2e, Honda Civic GX, and Nissan Leaf. China is pressuring General Motors for electric car technology.[13] Hybrid engines are already widely popular. For instance, models like the Toyota Prius combine a gasoline engine with an electric motor, delivering as much as fifty miles to the gallon.[14]

The question is whether electric cars will grow enough in popularity to be of significance in the years ahead. Meantime, auto manufacturers are facing the challenge of continually tougher Corporate Average Fuel Economy (CAFE) standards by the EPA in Washington, as well as state environmental regulatory bodies.

Energy: The Environmental Impact Factor

"The activist is not the man who says the river is dirty. The activist is the man who cleans up the river."

—Ross Perot

Carbon dioxide can remain in the atmosphere for more than a hundred years. Carbon dioxide concentrations are 380 ppm (parts per million) currently and are increasing at roughly 2 ppm per year.

At this time there are several means of cutting carbon dioxide emissions from vehicles: improving fuel efficiency, substituting cleaner fuels, or driving less. Although the government has a major say in the role of environmental preservation in the energy mix, ultimately it is you, the consumer, who will decide.[15]

Notes for Chapter 7

1. *Freedom from Oil.* p. 84.
2. Ibid.
3. *Popular Mechanics.* May 2006.
4. *Wall Street Journal.* Sept. 29, 2011.
5. Utah Solar Energy Association website, www.UTSolar.org.
6. *The Oklahoman.* June 16, 2011.
7. *Wall Street Journal.* October 1, 2011.
8. US Department of Energy website, www.EERE.energy.gov/basics/renewable_energy/photovoltaics.
9. *The Oklahoman.* July 8, 2011.
10. *The Oklahoman.* June 18, 2011.
11. *Oklahoma Gazette.* December 7, 2011.
12. *Freedom from Oil.* p. 69.
13. *New York Times.* September 7, 2011.
14. *Freedom from Oil.* p. 79.
15. Ibid., p. 31, 82.

Please use this space to make notes about this chapter for later reference.

Part III

Creating Together
the People's Energy Plan

8

Energy Security

"And I'm asking you for your good and for your nation's security to take no unnecessary trips, to use carpools or public transportation whenever you can, to park your car one extra day per week, to obey the speed limit, and to set your thermostats to save fuel. Every act of energy conservation like this is more than just common sense—I tell you it is an act of patriotism."

—President Jimmy Carter
Speech to the nation, "Energy and National Goals—
A Crisis of Confidence," July 15, 1979

Thirty years after President Carter gave this speech, the big unknowns are the same: Where is the price of gasoline headed, and what will be the future of energy in America? We are back to relying on the same tactics President Carter suggested in 1979—carpooling, taking public transportation, parking your car an extra day, and making sure to drive the speed limit. We are being forced to adjust our lifestyle just as we did back then. While Carter's prescription of conserving energy should have been important all along, energy conservation alone is not the total answer to our national energy security.

Energy security is based on an energy plan in which we all conserve but also determine how we will obtain more oil and gas, or wind power, or solar power, or any of the other alternative sources now becoming available, to meet the demand. It is one thing to conserve, but we still must have energy. Energy security ensures we have the reliable energy sources to meet our needs that are available within our own country, as well as from friendly neighbors in North America such as Canada and Mexico. The energy dependence we suffer today costs us economically in the form of high prices and lost jobs. If we develop the People's Energy Plan, it will lead us to economic prosperity and energy security.

Then: In 2008 the total crude oil imported from nations that were identified as threats was over six million barrels a day, nearly 51 percent of total US-imported oil. This was a very high percentage, given the fact that our relationship with many of these nations was strained, at best. Most of these nations were anti-American. Some speculate this anti-American sentiment was largely the result of our involvement in Iraq, but ill will toward the land of liberty had plagued us and the region for quite some time. The Middle East was unstable long before the Gulf War, largely as a result of social oppression and economic depression brought on by inequities of monarchies, government-owned industries, and widespread corruption.

Four years ago, the belief that we could meet the increase in demand for gasoline, maintain severe restrictions on exploration, and still enjoy low prices was unfounded. This led us to the next problem. As I stated in my remarks at the John Massey Annual Lectureship at Southeastern Oklahoma State University in 2009, "If you are not mad, motivated, or a combination of both by the time you leave here, I have not been successful. Because, while the oil and gas industry is down, there were those that wanted to tax us out of existence. We need to remember all those that have made great sacrifices for our country from the energy industry."

For instance, during World War II the British government, our ally, needed more oil to defeat the Germans. However, most of the oil they used was imported. Then oil was discovered in England's Sherwood Forest, but the British needed America's help because they did not have the technological know-how to drill and produce it. Under secret arrangements made in February 1943, the American government sent forty-four oil field workers from Oklahoma to assist. These employees from Oklahoma were known as the "Oil Patch Warriors."[1]

The drilling team and four rigs imported from the US contributed significantly to the British war effort by boosting production at the field near Duke's Wood from 300 barrels per day to 3,000 barrels per day in double quick time. By the time the drilling team from two Oklahoma companies sailed home in the spring of 1944, they had drilled 106 wells. In honor of their sacrifice, a monument was erected in Sherwood Forest by The Energy Advocates, a nonprofit organization that raised the money for the seven-foot-high statue of a driller, the "Oil Patch Warrior" (learn more about it at www.DukesWoodOilMuseum.co.uk).

The British experience during World War II was a lesson in the necessity of energy security. Yet, in 2008, growth in our energy supplies was being curtailed by a regulatory structure that had failed to keep pace with advances in technology, and often discouraged investment in desperately need facilities. Trillions of cubic feet of gas buried in locations around the United States were off limits to oil and gas exploration due to local, state, and federal restrictions. As the world struggled to produce the fuel to power the advancement of humankind, tensions rose between nations with energy reserves and those without.

War has been—and will always be—a costly means of procuring necessary resources, but peace can eradicate supply problems. As I stated at the Massey Lectureship, "However, can there be peace? Furthermore, despite peace, will there be enough resources to satisfy the world's thirst for energy? In both of these cases, the answer may be no. The world was attempting to procure resources at a frenzied pace, and this competition was an obstacle to peace. As for oil, it seemed we were approaching the sunset of its tenure as the dominant fuel. However, this sunset could lead to the rise of another fuel—natural gas." In my view, it looked as if America's future energy source would not be the black gold we had come to romanticize over the last hundred years—rather, natural gas looked to be the bridge between oil and the unknown energy of the next century.

Just four years ago, 22 percent of all new transit buses on order nationwide were powered by CNG. ConocoPhillips had announced the construction of a natural gas pipeline to be built from northern Alaska to the lower forty-eight states. Liquefied natural gas (LNG)—natural gas that has been temporarily converted to liquid form for transport—would become a bigger component of the energy equation over the next several years. LNG is transported to markets such as Japan in vessels, not pipelines, and given our abundance of natural gas, could become a potentially major new sector for the US energy industry. In 2004 LNG accounted for 7 percent of the world's energy. Despite the fact that natural gas would be a very significant factor in the years ahead, however, oil remained our dominant energy source, so the transition to a natural gas economy also presented us with our greatest challenge. It would take courage to make the critical and difficult decisions to transform the way we consume and produce energy.

At that time, 60 million residential customers and 5 million commercial and industrial customers were using natural gas. In the US, nearly 130,000 buses, taxis, delivery trucks, and other natural gas powered vehicles were on the road. Natural gas also generates electricity, so it was accounting for 80 percent of new capacity. The Honda Civic GX was selling at $25,000, $10,000 more than the standard Civic, and traveled only 170 miles.

Real threats to our energy security continued to exist, starting with geopolitical tensions. Vladimir Putin in Russia and Hugo Chavez in Venezuela were leading the charge toward authoritarian rule. Nigeria had record corruption within its borders. In late 2006, headlines read, "Oil Prices Creep Higher on Terror Fears, Nigeria Villagers Seize Oil Platforms, Australia Faces Blackouts." As I warned at the Massey

Lectureship, "Whether we like it or not, we are in a global economy. With that global economy comes the emotions of good news and bad news, therefore swings in the prices." Demand was so much the focus. Ninety-two percent of US households possessed a motor vehicle, with 25 percent owning three or more motor vehicles. In comparison, China and a great part of the globe wanted the luxuries that we have.

An increase in demand was inevitable, I projected. In the US the average person consumed around 2.8 gallons of gasoline per day. In Japan, the figure was 1.8 gallons, and in China .2 gallons. Brazil's state-owned oil producer Petrobras had purchased a large stake in a refinery in Okinawa. There was great room for growth in demand. As John Hess, chairman of the Hess Corporation, observed, "Given the long lead times of at least five to ten years from (a major) discovery to production, an oil crisis is coming and sooner than most people think. Unfortunately, we are behaving in ways that suggest we do not know there is a serious problem."[2]

Now: When we talk about national energy security today, we are talking about oil, particularly as it relates to the Middle East. But we cannot depend just on oil. While America's oil is very important, and we need to develop it, natural gas will be a great transition to the future. The key to energy security right now is going from an oil-driven to a natural-gas driven economy. At present, natural gas is a clean and abundant fuel, and we have a lot of it here in the US, so it makes sense that we stop being dependent on others and become dependent on ourselves. A big part of that solution is natural gas, but it should eventually encompass all forms of energy, whether hydrogen or whatever other sources are best. But at this time, natural gas should, be near the top of the list, if not at the top, because it is our own energy source. The natural gas we can rely on is not coming from the Middle East or any other foreign entity other than Canada.

As Brook Simmons reported in the Oklahoma Independent Petroleum Association's *Wellhead Magazine*, "Increased domestic oil production has helped shrink net US petroleum imports to 46 percent and imports from Persian Gulf nations to less than 18 percent. US natural gas supply is now measured in centuries." However, peak electricity demand during the summer of 2011 surged past levels that were not expected until 2014, revealing a potential shortage of generating capacity for the next several years.

In 2012 Iran threatened to close the Strait of Hormuz, the world's most important oil trade route. Almost 17 million barrels a day of oil flowed through it in 2011, which is approximately 20 percent of the oil found worldwide.[3] Meantime, OPEC continues its efforts to control oil pricing and worldwide production levels.

America, and for that matter, Oklahoma, needs to take the lead in energy leadership for us to achieve energy security. Throughout the speeches I make around the country, I state my belief that America should be the center for energy excellence because the world needs our expertise. "America Needs America's Energy and its Energy Leadership" is a theme of mine. I also advocate that Americans need to support the energy industry. The amount of federal land available for exploration needs to be broadened. All forms of energy will be necessary in the future. Education is a first and necessary step toward the solution.

Notes for Chapter 8
1. *Oil and Gas Journal.* June 24, 1991.
2. *Wall Street Journal.* February 20, 2008.
3. *Wall Street Journal.* January 7, 2012.

Please use this space to make notes about this chapter
for later reference.

9

Energy Education

> "I think most Americans would welcome messages from an industry expressly committed to the importance of what it does, confident in its ability to manage risks, and willing to defend its important work against extremist assault. Most Americans understand the need for secure supplies of affordable energy. And they always embrace conviction."
>
> —**Bob Tippee**
> Editor, *Oil and Gas Journal*, IEPC Roundtable
> November 10, 2011

At a White House briefing I attended in September 2006, I asked US Secretary of Energy Samuel Bodman about the status of then-pending national energy education initiatives. He did not have an answer, but promised he would have an aide contact me with answers. The aide did call, but provided me little information.[1] Energy education was needed then, as it is now.

This experience of mine years ago proves that when it comes to education about energy, a public-private partnership is necessary. One organization that has been in the forefront of this effort is the International Society of The Energy Advocates, a not-for-profit energy education organization founded in 1974 by a group of

American oil executives in response to the 1973–1974 oil embargo. The primary mission of The Energy Advocates is to inform the general public about our vital energy industry and energy policy issues. Since 1974 members of The Energy Advocates have spoken in all fifty states and appeared on television, radio, and in newspapers and magazines on behalf of the energy industry. The organization believes that it is critical for those of us in the energy business to rise to the challenge and make a difference when it comes to energy issues.

The goal of The Energy Advocates is to raise awareness and change the public's perception of the energy industry. For too long many have painted a misleading and false picture of the energy business. The Energy Advocates continually educates the public while improving the industry's image through forums, community involvement, speeches, seminars, monthly updates, media coverage, annual energy conferences, and resources on its website, www.EnergyAdvocates.org.

The Energy Advocates believe in the basic principle that "nothing moves without energy." Therefore, education begins by recognizing that energy is a basic requirement of life. Our quality of life is dependent upon the development of all forms of energy, as well as the conservation of our natural resources. The facts are clear: energy production and consumption work in concert with the environment. The organization is passionate about presenting the public with facts and solutions to tough questions on the energy issues that face the United States, including those related to our environment.

"Other than Wall Street, few other segments of the economy attract as much vitriol as the energy industry in general, and oil and gas, in particular," reported Paul Wiseman of the *Midland Telegram* in December 2011. "Realizing that just as much energy must be expended to clean up its public image as is spent on cleaning up an oil spill, spokesman Mark Stansberry of Oklahoma-based Energy Advocates is going on the road in 2012 as to both disburse and collect information."

As I explained to Wiseman in that article, what The Energy Advocates are trying to do is get out more and have more hands-on talks with people in different cities, making speeches, and hosting roundtables, conferences, whatever, especially in 2012. We want to learn what is on people's minds. From a national perspective, it should be creating the People's Energy Plan. But the message doesn't seem to be—as far as energy education—reaching everyone. The goal is to raise public awareness of the need for energy and that energy is not a bad thing. "Really, energy is our friend—nothing moves without energy," I pointed out, listing agriculture, transportation, and health care among other sectors that depend greatly on energy for their own survival (full text of the article can be found in the appendix).

Loren Steffy, a business columnist at the *Houston Chronicle*, commented on this article in his blog, saying, "One of the questions I am asked most frequently when I speak to the industry groups pertains to the industry's image and what can be done about it. I usually find myself talking about how the industry has done a poor job of handling its most visible disasters, and how because much of the energy industry has little direct contact with the public, the only time it finds itself in the spotlight is when something goes terribly wrong."[2]

Steffy is right in terms of the industry image being shaped solely when things go wrong. The challenge is for citizens, the industry, media, and others to maintain a continuing dialogue so that an energy policy of the people, by the people, and for the people can be implemented. And that implementation needs to take place now, not be put off to another time.

Another objective of The Energy Advocates is keeping the membership and general public informed of the changing legislative, environmental, and economic issues that impact the energy industry. As global demands for energy from natural resources respond to social, economic, and environmental factors, it is important to continue to inform and enlighten the public about the need for a vibrant energy industry.

Mission Statement

The Energy Advocates' mission is to educate the American public about its vital energy industry and energy policy issues in a balanced and unbiased manner.

Vision Statement

The Energy Advocates' vision is for America to achieve a clear and balanced energy policy that includes all forms of energy through grassroots initiatives.

Motto

"Nothing moves without energy."

Theme

"America needs America's energy!"

The International Energy Policy Conference (IEPC)

In 1992 I founded and chaired the first International Energy Policy Conference, which was held at the University of Oklahoma. The founding principle of IEPC remains steadfast: the availability of reasonably priced energy is paramount to economic and business development, both in the United States and in other countries around the world. It also greatly impacts many other aspects of human development globally. IEPC is a unique format developed through the years that provides a forum for companies, corporations, legislators, and organizations to provide vital input on this subject, as well as receive valuable information from industry leaders and specialists throughout the energy industry.

IEPC has been hosted by various sponsors, corporations, and organizations such as the Oklahoma Royalty Company, The Energy

Advocates, the Oklahoma State Chamber, the US Department of Energy, Sarkeys Energy Center at the University of Oklahoma, People to People International, the American Gas Association, Oklahoma Marginal Well Commission, and the World Alliance for Decentralized Energy. The involvement of these organizations has allowed the conference to grow each year.

IEPC also has a strong list of past honorary conference chairs, including former UN Ambassador Jeane Kirkpatrick (who served three times), former Oklahoma Governor Frank Keating, Oklahoma Lieutenant Governor Mary Fallin (currently governor of Oklahoma), Senator Don Nickles, Congressman Wes Watkins, Oklahoma Corporation Commissioner Denise Bode, Tulsa Mayor Bill LaFortune, James A. Beck, and US Ambassador to Saudi Arabia Robert Jordan.

Since 1998 The Energy Advocates has been a strong supporter of IEPC. Each year The Energy Advocates host their annual meetings, as well as honor their membership and others in the industry, at the conference with their annual Energy Advocate of the Year awards. Past Energy Advocate of the Year Award (Individual) recipients have included Christine Hansen, Liz Fajen, Dr. Charles Mankin, A. M. "Mac" Alloway, Aubrey McClendon, Harold Hamm, and Sherman Smith. The corporate awards have included Schlumberger, Chesapeake Energy, CEED, Ward Petroleum, AEP/PSO, Chickasaw Nation (Enterprises) along with its leaders Governor Bill Anoatubby and Brian Campbell, and Farmers National Company led by David Smith.

Lifetime award recipients have included John A. "Jack" Taylor, Sherman Smith, Wayne Swearingen, L. O. "Lew" Ward, Raymond Plank, Mac Alloway, T. Boone Pickens, and Robert Hefner III. Association award recipients have included the Oklahoma Independent Petroleum Association, Texas Alliance of Energy Producers, and the National Association of Royalty Owners led by Tina Bonner and Jerry Simmons. Journalism awards have gone to media recipients, including KFAQ 1170AM radio in Tulsa, the *Tulsa World, Wall Street Journal*, Bob Tippee at *Oil and Gas Journal*, and the *Tulsa Beacon*.

Past conferences have been held in Washington, DC, Tulsa, Denver, Dallas, Houston, and Oklahoma City. In 2012 the conference will return to the campus of the University of Oklahoma and to Oklahoma City. Due to the leadership of David Boren, president of the University of Oklahoma, who is also a former US senator from Oklahoma and former governor of Oklahoma, we are able to bring the 2012 conference back to the campus where it began twenty years ago. Boren is a longtime leader in supporting the development of an energy plan for the US.

The Energy Advocates, in association with the Chickasaw Nation and Governor Anoatubby, will host the 2012 conference. The theme is "Water Resources and The Future of Energy."

IEPC Conference Theme

When we started our conference in 1992, we were ahead of our time by pushing for "Striving for Energy Efficiency and Environmental Preservation" as a theme. This theme remains our umbrella theme today, with numerous subtopics addressed at each conference.

To learn more about IEPC and the resources it offers, visit www.EnergyPolicyConference.com.

Roundtables Sponsored by The Energy Advocates

For the past two years The Energy Advocates has held a continuous schedule of roundtables and city visits throughout the US including these locations: Amarillo, Wichita, Ft. Smith, Dallas, Kansas City, Washington, DC, Austin, Houston, Los Angeles, Missoula, Oklahoma City, and Tulsa.

At these roundtables I begin by summarizing the existing market conditions that impact our energy situation today, starting with projected growth in global demand that again appears on the uptick. At the same time, inadequate energy policy is impeding the continued development of energy supplies, and our energy infrastructure is inadequate.

From there, I touch on the various aspects that our national energy policy should encompass, including manpower, research and development, technological advancement, governmental lands opened up for exploration, and expansion of refining. I stress in my presentation how we must remember that the oil and gas industry suffered from twenty plus years of underinvestment. From the 1980s to only a few years ago, the oil and gas industry lost close to a half a million jobs.

These roundtables are especially pertinent to today's college business students, who face tremendous challenges and great opportunities ahead. Once they enter the working world, they will have to make decisions such as which car is best for them to drive, as well as their employees. Which fuels will they choose—a hydrogen-powered auto or an electric plug-in? Energy management and conservation decisions will affect their daily lives, both personally and professionally, so keeping up with the latest policy implications will be necessary for them to succeed. My hope is that they will become leaders who seek solutions, leaders who study history, learn from it, and build on those lessons.

The response from those who have attended our roundtables has been very positive. For example, a student who had attended The Fund for American Studies program at Georgetown University and participated in one of roundtables wrote me, "I enjoyed the roundtable so much that it prompted me to enroll in a natural resources and environmental economics course. I am beginning to work on a research paper on how our nation's energy policy should be structured and improved." The student also sought my advice on the best texts and research to learn more, as well as insight on graduate schools and possible career paths involving energy policy. The student's e-mail concluded, "The roundtable was one of the highlights of my time in Washington, DC."

In addition to students who have participated, over the years we have held these sessions with civic leaders, business people, members of the federal energy regulatory body, attorneys, and those interested in alternative energy sources like biomass and wind power. Participants report that the experience helps them evaluate not just where they are as individuals, but as companies, schools, and employers. We talk about the various fuels available and how they can incorporate those—or whether they should in their particular area. They look at what they are driving now and think about what they plan to drive five years from then. We get them thinking about how they intend to help society as it relates to energy in the future. The roundtables also give them an evaluation of their particular city or region from an energy standpoint.

Ultimately, the roundtable discussions make those in attendance question what we are doing in this country to strive for energy efficiency and environmental preservation for our future. They return home enthusiastic, feeling they are no longer alone in their efforts, but motivated to go back out into their communities and schools to encourage the process of creating an energy plan. Until now, this process has gone rather slowly. My hope is that this book will inspire it to move much faster. I am encouraged in this hope because in my visits around the country to cities like Austin and Nashville, I find people are already working to become more energy efficient, striving to develop an energy plan. They are working together in this country's best interest to be sure we have the proper energy sources lined up to meet our needs in the future.

If you want to learn more about our roundtables, or request a roundtable be held in your city, visit www.EnergyPolicyConference.com or www.EnergyAdvocates.org.

Notes for Chapter 9
1. White House Briefing. September 2006.
2. Steffy, Loren. *Houston Chronicle* Business Blog. December 8, 2011.

Please use this space to make notes about this chapter for later reference.

10

Creating Together the People's Energy Plan

"Without reliable energy, the world economy and world institutions would devolve to chaos."

—**Irma S. Russell**
in the *Tulsa Law Review*[1]

Why an energy plan? And why now? To answer those questions, you need to understand that there are two parties involved in creating the People's Energy Plan:

The Players

You the consumer. You the investor. We are all stakeholders in our energy future!

The Opposition

The opposition against the energy industry has been identified as environmentalists. However, during the thirty-five years I have spent in the energy business, I have strongly supported protecting the environment, as do most of those in the energy industry. In fact, our motto for the IEPC International Energy

Policy Conference over the last twenty years has been "Striving for Energy Efficiency and Environmental Preservation." It is time for the environmentalists and energy industry to come together to achieve a common goal.

Infrastructure and Production Needs

"Under the rule of the 'free market ideology,' we have gone through two decades of an energy crisis without an effective energy policy. Because of an easy and thoughtless reliance on imported oil, we have no adequate policy for the conservation of gasoline and other petroleum products. We have no adequate policy for the development or use of other, less harmful forms of energy. We have no adequate system of public transportation."

—Wendell Berry
"Peaceableness Toward Enemies," *Sex, Economy, Freedom & Community*

As the information presented in this book makes clear, America's energy industry has an infrastructure that must be updated, and increasing the number of drilling permits could create thousands of jobs and add billions of dollars to the US gross domestic product. As previously explained, these permit increases would add revenue to state and federal budgets and in the end reduce spending on foreign oil by $15 billion.[2] To accomplish these goals, though, requires money. It will take an accommodation of both the public and private sectors to come together for the solutions, so we definitely have to have the marriage of both, but also a policy in place. We must set the agenda for our energy, starting today.

Richard S. Lugar, the senator for Indiana, stated it best: "Good policy emerges from serious debate, informed by the facts. Today we need bold new approaches for forging bipartisan coalitions."[3]

A recent editorial in *The Oklahoman* echoed his sentiment: "The default setting for a national energy policy in this country is inertia. We don't do much to advance a policy to promote greater independence. We actually do some things to promote more reliance on foreign supplies. But mostly we sit around and talk about the need for a comprehensive energy plan. While we're talking, the supply of energy is walking and it's moving west, from the Mideast to Americas. Decreasing foreign oil dependence is happening by default and it's happening because of technology and free enterprise and despite US government policy and interference."[4]

The point of this editorial is critical. Because of the recent increase in production here, there are rumblings that the government may start taxing oil and gas companies on the exploration and production sides of it. So now we are in a position where we find this wondrous new discovery but are faced with new taxes and regulations to burden us. Despite our government not doing what they should be doing, we don't want them to start interfering again. Since we have gone the extra route of finding the equivalent of Saudi Arabian oil in the US, we need to make certain we have the right incentives and not interference.

In the acknowledgements to his book *Capitol Betrayal*, best-selling author William Bernhardt stated, "As you may have gathered, Ben Kincaid feels strongly that we need to end our dependence on oil and move to natural gas and other alternatives as soon as possible. The best discussion of these issues I've read is in a book called *The Braking Point: America's Energy Dreams and Global Economic Realities*, by my friends Mark Stansberry and Jason P. Reimbold."

This book, *America Needs America's Energy*, is a follow-up book to our nation's ongoing journey toward an energy future. A strong energy industry, as we are seeing today in the shale activity in North Dakota and Pennsylvania, means more jobs and a more secure economy.

As I emphasized in *The Braking Point*: "Thirty years ago I began a journey in the energy industry. Hopefully, we will leave a great energy industry in place for future generations. It is up to us! America Needs

America's Energy!" Today, that message has greater meaning than ever before. Nothing moves without energy! American needs you to get involved! *America needs America's energy!*

Your Personal Energy Journal 2012–2016

America's energy future is in our hands. We can no longer wait for the government to rally us. History has shown this will not happen. The time has come for all of us, the people, to take control of our energy future here in America. That starts with us keeping a Personal Energy Journal, which will assist us in planning and executing our personal energy plans.

To give you an idea of what some cities are already doing to assist citizens in this process, at the end of this chapter I've included a sample copy of a standard report that homeowners in metropolitan Nashville receive following a voluntary in-home energy evaluation (audit). This Energy Action Plan shows participants the projected energy savings associated with each recommended measure.[5]

Following that, you will find your Personal Energy Journal forms for the years 2012 through 2016. These forms are a compilation of questions I have gathered from various sources I have encountered while speaking to groups and educating the public on energy policy.

Please join me in developing your own personal path to an energy strategy by completing these forms, which will guide you in assessing how you are personally using energy and understanding how the way you use energy as a consumer impacts energy issues and development.

The idea is to create your own personal energy plan for 2012 based on the evaluation, then develop it for the next five years. For instance, your goal for 2013 may be to convert your car to CNG, or add solar panels to your home, or investigate alternative energy sources such as wind available in your area. At the end of 2013, you can then check to see if you have met your goals. If not, you can either adjust your goals for the next few years or list the steps needed to achieve your personal energy goals in the near future. You may want to include others in this initial planning stage, such as your family, your company, or your organization.

As you proceed with creating your Personal Energy Journal, you'll find a lot of helpful background information in the first two parts of this book, including the pros and cons of the various energy alternatives currently available. In addition, in the back of the book you will find a glossary of energy terms, suggested reading, and web links that offer further assistance. But don't count on what you have read in this book alone. Do your homework. The energy industry is moving forward in innovation and technological advancement, so try to stay current with the latest information available.

You will find that your Personal Energy Journal will become a part of your journey into understanding the need for the People's Energy Plan, as well as a statement of your personal policy of striving for energy efficiency and environmental preservation. Once you have created your Personal Energy Plan, you can encourage other entities in your neighborhood or local area to create their own energy plan, including businesses, schools, and hospitals. In that way we will obtain the information we need to create a comprehensive regional, state, and national energy plan driven by the grassroots.

Conclusion

"Help us to harness the wind, the water, the sun, and all the ready and renewable sources of power. Teach us to conserve, preserve, use wisely the blessed treasures of our wealth-stored earth. Help us to share your bounty, not waste it, or pervert it into peril for our children or our neighbors in other nations. You, who are life and energy and blessing, teach us to revere and respect your tender world."

—Prayer of Thomas John Carlisle

In 2004, when I served as keynote speaker of the annual meeting of Merit Energy in Dallas, I announced that I had begun to write *The Braking Point*. The book was released four years later in 2008. Now we have reached 2012, and we are definitely beyond the braking point. But the good news is that we are not beyond getting America on the right track for putting forward an American Energy Plan! As I stated in *The Braking Point* and repeat today, "The need is for an American Energy Plan!" Together, we can make a difference. You can—and must—get involved today!

Energy Goals And Plans

2012:

2013:

2014:

2015:

2016:

Notes for Chapter 10

1. Russell, Irma S. *The Sustainability Principle in Sustainable Energy.* 44 Tulsa L. Rev. 891 (Symposium on Sustainability) (2008).
2. Green, Kenneth P. American Enterprise Institute for Public Policy Research. August 2011.
3. Lugar, Richard S. Foreword to *Freedom from Oil.*
4. *The Oklahoman.* December 7, 2011.
5. Mayor's Office of Environmental and Sustainability. Nashville, Tennessee.

Please use this space to make notes about this chapter
for later reference.

Example of IHEE Energy Audit Form

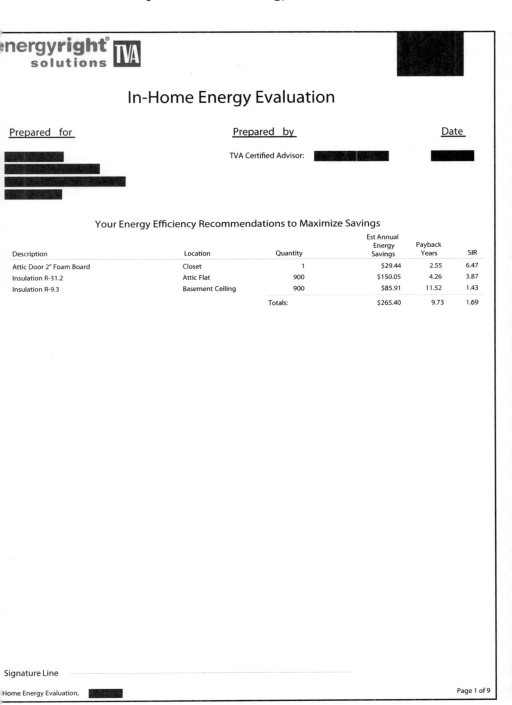

energyright® solutions TVA

In-Home Energy Evaluation

Prepared for   **Prepared by**   **Date**

TVA Certified Advisor:

Your Energy Efficiency Recommendations to Maximize Savings

Description	Location	Quantity	Est Annual Energy Savings	Payback Years	SIR
Attic Door 2" Foam Board	Closet	1	$29.44	2.55	6.47
Insulation R-31.2	Attic Flat	900	$150.05	4.26	3.87
Insulation R-9.3	Basement Ceiling	900	$85.91	11.52	1.43
		Totals:	$265.40	9.73	1.69

Signature Line

Home Energy Evaluation,

In-Home Energy Evaluation

Prepared for   **Prepared by**   **Date**

TVA Certified Advisor:

Your Energy Efficiency Recommendations to Maximize Savings

Regarding the Savings Estimates

Procedures used to make these estimates are consistent with criteria established by the U.S. Department of Energy and the Tennessee Valley Authority *energy right®* In-Home Energy Evaluation standards for residential energy evaluations. Actual savings may be different from estimates contained in this report.

Estimated Annual Energy Savings from installing more than one measure may be less than the sum of energy cost savings of measures installed individually. Estimated savings are based on the current retail fuel and electricity costs; they do not account for future price escalation or inflation.

Payback Years indicates the estimated amount of time it will take before the cost of investing in a recommended measure is earned back through energy savings.

Savings to Investment Ratio (SIR) estimates the relationship between a recommended measure's savings and its investment cost. The SIR can be used to rank the relative importance of recommended measures. As a general rule of thumb, installing a measure with an SIR equal to or greater than "1" is a financially sound decision because the overall savings are greater than the investment cost.

Thank you for taking the first step for a more affordable, comfortable, and environmentally friendly home.

Signature Line

Residential Report

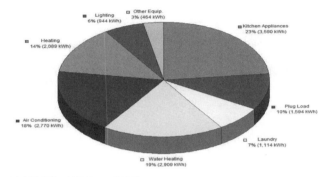

TVA Residential Electricity Consumption By End-Use
All Households - FY08

- Other Equip. 3% (464 kWh)
- Lighting 6% (944 kWh)
- Heating 14% (2,089 kWh)
- Kitchen Appliances 23% (3,580 kWh)
- Plug Load 10% (1,594 kWh)
- Air Conditioning 18% (2,770 kWh)
- Laundry 7% (1,114 kWh)
- Water Heating 19% (2,909 kWh)

FY08 TVA Average Annual Residential Consumption = 15,475 kWh
(Source: TVA Electricity Sales Statistics)

115

About Your Recommended Energy Efficiency Measures

Air Sealing

Excessive air infiltrating the home through small gaps and crevices wastes 25% of the typical home's heating and cooling costs. In the winter, cold air leaks into the home, while heated air exits. In the summer, hot outside air enters the home and brings unwanted humidity. This is caused by large (often unseen) holes in the attic and crawlspace, floor and ceiling joints, electrical and plumbing penetrations, and even small cracks and gaps around windows and doors. While any one of these gaps may appear minor, collectively they can have the same effect as leaving a window wide open all year long. Air infiltration can also cause water vapor to condense inside walls and ceilings, causing mildew and structural damage, and causing insulation to become wet and ineffective. While it is possible to make a home too air-tight, more than 90% of homes are much too drafty. Your Energy Advisor has determined your home probably has excessive air infiltration and could benefit from professional air sealing services.

Attic Insulation

Attic/ceiling insulation reduces conductive heat transfer between your home and the attic space outside the home. Attics are often the easiest and most cost-effective place to insulate because most attics provide easy access for the installations. The ready access and lower installation cost often make this a very cost-effective measure. Attic insulation is most effective when the ceiling plane between the home and the attic space is tightly air sealed. Like all insulation, ceiling insulation helps keep the home warm in the winter and cool in the summer.

Adding insulation above your ceiling can be very cost-effective, depending on the pre-existing insulation levels. The first few inches of insulation provide the greatest energy savings. While adding layers will improve energy efficiency, each layer is somewhat less effective than the first layers. Ceilings should be insulated to R-30 or greater. This usually amounts to about 10 inches of glass fiber or cellulose. If the current insulation level above your ceilings is already R-22 or greater, it may or may not be cost-effective to add insulation. The current insulation level is included in the financial analysis of this report. We strongly recommend air sealing the home before installing any insulation in the attic.

Electric Water Heater Insulation

Installing additional insulation on the exterior of your electric water heater can help prevent heat from escaping your water heater. If your water heater is warm to the touch, heat is escaping and increasing your energy bill.

bout Your Recommended Energy Efficiency Measures

loor Insulation

Floor insulation reduces conductive heat transfer between your home's floor and an unheated crawlspace or basement. Floor insulation usually consists of placing fiberglass batting between the floor joists underneath the floor of the living space. Floor insulation helps keep the home warm in the winter and cool in the summer. Because the air temperature of unheated basements and crawlspaces are somewhat tempered by the earth, insulating the floors will not be as effective compared to walls or ceilings. Home owners should examine both the estimated costs and annual savings of every measure on the evaluation report to determine priorities for implementing energy efficiency measures.

Adding insulation in your floors can be cost-effective and improve the comfort of your home. We recommend installing insulation between the floor joists and the unheated basement or crawlspace. Insulating in this manner will keep your home warmer in the winter, and lower your utility bills. It is very important to install a continuous and sealed vapor barrier (plastic sheeting) on the ground of crawlspaces to prevent moisture from collecting in the insulation. Damp insulation harbors mildew and can damage the structure of the home. If water ever collects in the crawlspace or basement, you must remedy the drainage problem before installing a vapor barrier or insulating the floor.

ot Water Pipe Insulation

Water pipe insulation installed at the water heater is a cost-effective way to reduce heat loss through water pipes. It can reduce heat loss through the pipes during delivery of the hot water, in addition to standby losses in both hot and cold water lines. Insulated pipes deliver water 2°F to 4°F hotter than uninsulated pipes, allowing you to lower the temperature setting on the heater. Polyethylene or neoprene foam pipe sleeves are the most common pipe insulation. The inside diameter of the pipe insulation should match the outside diameter of the pipe to ensure a snug fit. Pipes within 8" of a combustion flue should be insulated with at least 1" fiberglass pipe wrap without a facing.

ehab Work

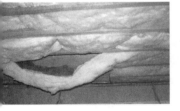

Rehabilitation work of existing conditions within a house is sometimes an important pre-requisite to increase the effectiveness and efficiency of newly installed improvements. In other cases, rehabilitation work is needed to restore the effectiveness and efficiency of improvements that are already installed in your home.

117

Financial Incentives Available to You

General Financial Incentive Requirements:

1. You have the option to apply for a cash incentive OR financing (not available in all areas).
2. You must spend at least $150 on eligible recommended installation measures to qualify for a cash incentive and reimbursement of the evaluation fee.
3. Only eligible recommended installation measures may qualify for a cash incentive.
4. Total cash incentives for all eligible recommended installation measures will not exceed $500.
5. You may not participate in the *energy right®* Heat Pump Program within 6 months from the date of this In-Home Energy Evaluation.
6. All work must be performed by a Quality Contractor Network member.
7. All work must be performed in compliance with *energy right®* standards and requirements.
8. All work must pass a quality control inspection following completion of the installation.

Floor Insulation

The energy evaluation data suggests that your home would benefit from floor insulation. The TVA *energy right®* In-Home Energy Evaluation Program offers a 50% cash incentive up to $500 for floor insulation.

Water Pipe Insulation

The energy evaluation data suggests that your home would benefit from water pipe insulation. The TVA *energy right®* In-Home Energy Evaluation Program offers a 50% cash incentive up to $50 for water pipe insulation.

Electric Water Heater Insulation

The energy evaluation data suggests that your home would benefit from water heater insulation. The TVA *energy right®* In-Home Energy Evaluation Program offers a 50% cash incentive up to $50 for insulation of an electric water heater.

Air Sealing

The evaluation data suggests your home would benefit from air sealing. The TVA *energy right®* In-Home Energy Evaluation Program offers a 50% cash incentive up to $500 for air sealing.

Financial Incentive Requirements:

1. Your home must have a working carbon monoxide (CO) monitor before any air sealing may be performed.

Financial Incentives Available to You

Attic Insulation and Ventilation

Based on the data collected during the energy evaluation, your home qualifies for financial incentives to insulate your attic. The TVA *energy right®* In-Home Energy Evaluation Program offers a 50% cash incentive up to $500 for insulating and ventilating your attic.

Financial Incentive Requirements:

1. Attic ventilation must be non-powered.
2. Your home must have a working carbon monoxide (CO) monitor before any attic insulation may be installed.

Rehabilitation Work

The energy evaluation data suggests that your home would benefit from certain rehabilitation work. The TVA *energy right®* In-Home Energy Evaluation Program offers a 50% cash incentive up to $250 for rehabilitation work recommended by your Energy Advisor.

Financial Incentive Requirement:

1. Work must be one of the following measures:
   repair of broken glass
   window glazing
   prime door replacement
   removal of attic fan and resulting repair
   reinstallation of kneewall insulation
   reinstallation of floor insulation

Option to Finance

The TVA *energy right*° In-Home Energy Evaluation Program offers an option to finance eligible recommended improvements installed in your home, subject to credit approval:

☐ Rate : 6%.
☐ Limits : minimum $1,500; maximum $20,000 (includes up to $10,000 for a single all electric heat pump or dual fuel heat pump; or $12,500 for an advanced heat pump or multiple all electric heat pumps). Actual financing limits may vary by power distributor and total loan indebtedness to a power distributor may not exceed the maximum loan amount. Please check with your Energy Advisor or power distributor for details.
☐ Term : up to 10 years (3 years if heat & air equipment is not financed).
☐ Payments : due and payable via your monthly utility bill.
☐ Requirements : Choose either the financing option or the cash incentive option. Please note that Replacement Windows and self installed measures are not eligible for financing.

For more information on the financing option, please call your Energy Advisor.

Important for You to Know

Combustion Appliance Safety

Measures such as air sealing, duct sealing and insulation of closed cavities like walls and cathedral ceilings save energy in whole or in part by reducing excessive air flow into and out of the home. When these measures are installed in a home with combustion appliances such as heating equipment, ovens, fireplaces and water heaters, it is imperative that they are tested for proper operation.

Gas fired appliances which take their combustion air from the inside of the home can present a toxic hazard from carbon monoxide and other gases if there is inadequate combustion air or the burner does not receive sufficient oxygen. All homes with unvented gas fireplaces, gas space heaters or other gas-fired appliances should have a **carbon monoxide monitor** in the room where the appliance is located. If you smell gas or fumes of any kind, you should have your appliances tested by a qualified gas specialist.

Additional Recommendations

Description	Location	Quantity
Carbon Monoxide (CO) Monitor	All Existing	2
Air Sealing without Blower Door	Unspecified	4
Water Pipe Insulation 1/2"x1/2"x3'	Unspecified	2
Electric Water Heater Insulation	Basement	1
Fiberglass Exterior Door	Basement	1

Weatherization Specifics

Description
Weatherstripping

Form provided by the mayor's office of Nashville.

Individual Evaluation Energy Charts
2012

INDIVIDUAL ENERGY USE EVALUATION CHART

To better understand your energy consumption and or energy footprint, please fill out the following form, estimated in monthly increments, then multiply the total(s) by 12 months. Estimations are acceptable for this purpose. However, the more accurate the estimations, the more accurate view of your energy use will be.

Personal Hygiene

1. Do you leave the water running while Brushing Your Teeth? (Y / N)

Brushing your teeth can use 1-2 gallons of water if left running, per brush.

2. How many Gallons of Water used running a shower/bath per month?
(Estimate how many hours per person, then add them together to get total)

Monthly	For Year 2012

The estimated cost to heat enough water for a 10 minute shower (15-30 gallons per shower) 30 times per month is $20.11.

3. How many times do you Flush the Toilet?
(Estimate on a monthly basis per person in household)

Monthly	For Year 2012

An average person uses about 123 gallons (466 liters) of water daily. Flushing the toilet can use up to 5-7 gallons per day.

Household

4. How many Light-bulbs Do You Use in your home?

Monthly	For Year 2012

5. Fluorescent (Y / N) Incandescent (Y / N) Mixture of both (Y / N)

2012

6. How many hours are Lights Left In Use/On per month?

Monthly   For Year 2012

A typical incandescent light-bulb running 8 hours a day every day costs $18.25 per year while a florescent bulb running the same is $14.60. Multiply this total by the amount of bulbs in your in use within your house.

7. How many hours do you use the AC/Heat per month?

Monthly   For Year 2012

The average Central AC system (2.5 tons) can use 3500 watts per hour of continuous use. A medium sized window unit consumes 900 watts.

8. How many times do you Change Your Air Filter per month?

Monthly   For Year 2012

Changing your air filter frequently helps your heat and air systems run more efficiently, saving you money.

9. How many Batteries (AAA, AA, C, D, etc.) do you use in a month?

Monthly   For Year 2012

Depending on the size/wattage of the battery, costs for battery packages can range from $2.50 - $5+. Take into account the size and how many batteries you use for various use.

10. What is the monthly average of your Gas/Heating Oil Bill?

Monthly   For Year 2012

The average US Gas utility bill runs $20-$35 in the summer, and $100-200+ in the winter depending on the size of your house and the severity of the winter. It can be less than $100 if you have a small house where it doesn't get too cold.

2012

11. What is the monthly average of your Electric Bill?

Monthly   For Year 2012

The average US electric utility bill runs near $50-$75 in the summer, and $100-200+ in the winter depending on the size of your house and the severity of the winter. It can be less than $100 if you have a small house/apartment where it doesn't get too cold.

12. How many hours of Cooking with Gas/Electric do you do monthly?

Monthly   For Year 2012

13. How many Loads of Laundry do you do per month?

Monthly   For Year 2012

The average cost of doing 15 loads of laundry in a Hot/Warm Rinse cycle and ⊠ full dryer costs $16.16.

14. How many hours do you spend Doing Dishes?
(If running dishwasher, estimate time that it runs start to finish)

Monthly   For Year 2012

Running the average dishwasher for 15 loads per month (9-12 gallons per load) for a full cycle costs $19.15 per month.

15. How many pots of coffee do you brew per month?

Monthly   For Year 2012

The average coffee maker cost 2.6¢ per brew.

Entertainment

16. How many Hours of Television do you watch on a monthly basis?

Monthly   For Year 2012

A 40"-42" LCD on average costs $41 per year to run.

2012

17. How many Hours Do You Spend Online?

Monthly	For Year 2012

Personal Computer and Monitor: [(120 Watts + 150 Watts) ▢ 4 hours/day ▢ 365 days/year] ÷ 1000 = 394 kWh ▢ 8.5 cents/kWh = $33.51/year

18. How often would you say that you Eat/Dine Out?
(Estimate time(s) per month)

Monthly	For Year 2012

19. The times you Dine Out, how many are "Fast Food" establishments?

Monthly	For Year 2012

The EPA estimates each person throws away around 10-15 pounds of food each week. Fast Food ads to this amount with packaging of food and drink items as well as bagging and other containers.

20. How Many Handheld Devices do you have/use?
(Includes Cell Phones, iPod/mp3 Player, iPad/Tablet, Etc.)

Monthly	For Year 2012

21. How many Hours of Charging Handheld Devices per month?
(Estimate hours per device, then multiply by number of devices you have)

Monthly	For Year 2012

22. How many hours do you talk on a Land-line Phone per month?

Monthly	For Year 2012

2012

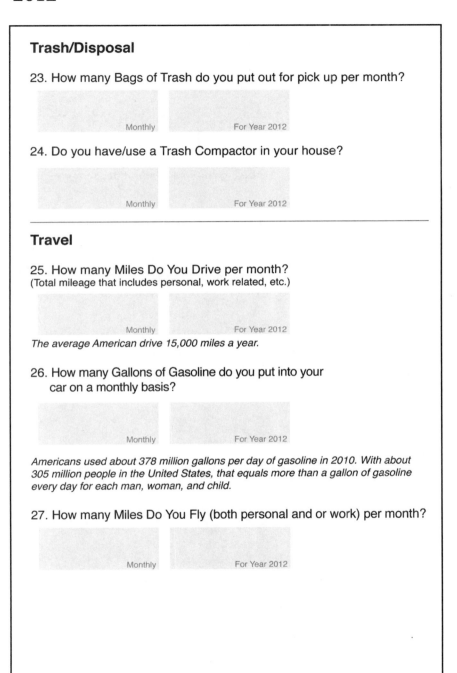

Trash/Disposal

23. How many Bags of Trash do you put out for pick up per month?

Monthly   For Year 2012

24. Do you have/use a Trash Compactor in your house?

Monthly   For Year 2012

Travel

25. How many Miles Do You Drive per month?
(Total mileage that includes personal, work related, etc.)

Monthly   For Year 2012

The average American drive 15,000 miles a year.

26. How many Gallons of Gasoline do you put into your
car on a monthly basis?

Monthly   For Year 2012

Americans used about 378 million gallons per day of gasoline in 2010. With about 305 million people in the United States, that equals more than a gallon of gasoline every day for each man, woman, and child.

27. How many Miles Do You Fly (both personal and or work) per month?

Monthly   For Year 2012

2012

Curious what your appliances might cost?

You can use this formula to estimate an appliance's energy use: (Wattage ☐ Hours Used Per Day) ÷ 1000 = Daily Kilowatt-hour (kWh) consumption 1 kilowatt (kW) = 1,000 Watts

National average electricity rate is: 8.5¢ per kWh

Typical Wattage of Various Appliances

Here are some examples of the range of nameplate wattage for various household appliances:
Aquarium = 50–1210 Watts
Clock radio = 10
Coffee maker = 900–1200
Clothes washer = 350–500
Clothes dryer = 1800–5000
Dishwasher = 1200–2400
(using the drying feature greatly increases energy consumption)
Dehumidifier = 785
Electric blanket- Single/Double = 60 / 100
Ceiling fan = 65–175
Window fan = 55–250
Furnace = 750
Whole house = 240–750
Hair dryer = 1200–1875
Heater (portable) = 750–1500
Clothes iron = 1000–1800
Microwave oven = 750–1100
Personal computer
CPU - awake / asleep = 120 / 30 or less
Monitor - awake / asleep = 150 / 30 or less
Laptop = 50
Radio (stereo) = 70–400
Refrigerator (frost-free, 16 cubic feet) = 725
Televisions (color)
19" = 65–110
27" = 113
36" = 133
53"-61" Projection = 170
Flat screen = 120
Toaster = 800–1400
Toaster oven = 1225
VCR/DVD = 17–21 / 20–25
Vacuum cleaner = 1000–1440
Water heater (40 gallon) = 4500–5500
Water pump (deep well) = 250–1100
Water bed (with heater, no cover) = 120–380

2013

INDIVIDUAL ENERGY USE EVALUATION CHART

To better understand your energy consumption and or energy footprint, please fill out the following form, estimated in monthly increments, then multiply the total(s) by 12 months. Estimations are acceptable for this purpose. However, the more accurate the estimations, the more accurate view of your energy use will be.

Personal Hygiene

1. Do you leave the water running while Brushing Your Teeth? (Y / N)

Brushing your teeth can use 1-2 gallons of water if left running, per brush.

2. How many Gallons of Water used running a shower/bath per month?
(Estimate how many hours per person, then add them together to get total)

Previous Year	Monthly	For Year 2013

The estimated cost to heat enough water for a 10 minute shower (15-30 gallons per shower) 30 times per month is $20.11.

3. How many times do you Flush the Toilet?
(Estimate on a monthly basis per person in household)

Previous Year	Monthly	For Year 2013

An average person uses about 123 gallons (466 liters) of water daily. Flushing the toilet can use up to 5-7 gallons per day.

Household

4. How many Light-bulbs Do You Use in your home?

Monthly	For Year 2012	For Year 2013

5. Fluorescent (Y / N) Incandescent (Y / N) Mixture of both (Y / N)

2013

6. How many hours are Lights Left In Use/On per month?

Previous Year	Monthly	For Year 2013

A typical incandescent light-bulb running 8 hours a day every day costs $18.25 per year while a florescent bulb running the same is $14.60. Multiply this total by the amount of bulbs in your in use within your house.

7. How many hours do you use the AC/Heat per month?

Previous Year	Monthly	For Year 2013

The average Central AC system (2.5 tons) can use 3500 watts per hour of continuous use. A medium sized window unit consumes 900 watts.

8. How many times do you Change Your Air Filter per month?

Previous Year	Monthly	For Year 2013

Changing your air filter frequently helps your heat and air systems run more efficiently, saving you money.

9. How many Batteries (AAA, AA, C, D, etc.) do you use in a month?

Previous Year	Monthly	For Year 2013

Depending on the size/wattage of the battery, costs for battery packages can range from $2.50 - $5+. Take into account the size and how many batteries you use for various use.

10. What is the monthly average of your Gas/Heating Oil Bill?

Previous Year	Monthly	For Year 2013

The average US Gas utility bill runs $20-$35 in the summer, and $100-200+ in the winter depending on the size of your house and the severity of the winter. It can be less than $100 if you have a small house where it doesn't get too cold.

2013

11. What is the monthly average of your Electric Bill?

Previous Year	Monthly	For Year 2013

The average US electric utility bill runs near $50-$75 in the summer, and $100-200+ in the winter depending on the size of your house and the severity of the winter. It can be less than $100 if you have a small house/apartment where it doesn't get too cold.

12. How many hours of Cooking with Gas/Electric do you do monthly?

Previous Year	Monthly	For Year 2013

13. How many Loads of Laundry do you do per month?

Previous Year	Monthly	For Year 2013

The average cost of doing 15 loads of laundry in a Hot/Warm Rinse cycle and ⊠ full dryer costs $16.16.

14. How many hours do you spend Doing Dishes?
(If running dishwasher, estimate time that it runs start to finish)

Previous Year	Monthly	For Year 2013

Running the average dishwasher for 15 loads per month (9-12 gallons per load) for a full cycle costs $19.15 per month.

15. How many pots of coffee do you brew per month?

Previous Year	Monthly	For Year 2013

The average coffee maker cost 2.6¢ per brew.

Entertainment

16. How many Hours of Television do you watch on a monthly basis?

Previous Year	Monthly	For Year 2013

A 40"-42" LCD on average costs $41 per year to run.

17. How many Hours Do You Spend Online?

Previous Year	Monthly	For Year 2013

Personal Computer and Monitor: [(120 Watts + 150 Watts) □ 4 hours/day □ 365 days/year] ÷ 1000 = 394 kWh □ 8.5 cents/kWh = $33.51/year

18. How often would you say that you Eat/Dine Out?
(Estimate time(s) per month)

Previous Year	Monthly	For Year 2013

19. The times you Dine Out, how many are "Fast Food" establishments?

Previous Year	Monthly	For Year 2013

The EPA estimates each person throws away around 10-15 pounds of food each week. Fast Food ads to this amount with packaging of food and drink items as well as bagging and other containers.

20. How Many Handheld Devices do you have/use?
(Includes Cell Phones, iPod/mp3 Player, iPad/Tablet, Etc.)

Previous Year	Monthly	For Year 2013

21. How many Hours of Charging Handheld Devices per month?
(Estimate hours per device, then multiply by number of devices you have)

Previous Year	Monthly	For Year 2013

22. How many hours do you talk on a Land-line Phone per month?

Previous Year	Monthly	For Year 2013

2013

Trash/Disposal

23. How many Bags of Trash do you put out for pick up per month?

Previous Year	Monthly	For Year 2013

24. Do you have/use a Trash Compactor in your house?

Previous Year	Monthly	For Year 2013

Travel

25. How many Miles Do You Drive per month?
(Total mileage that includes personal, work related, etc.)

Previous Year	Monthly	For Year 2013

The average American drive 15,000 miles a year.

26. How many Gallons of Gasoline do you put into your car on a monthly basis?

Previous Year	Monthly	For Year 2013

Americans used about 378 million gallons per day of gasoline in 2010. With about 305 million people in the United States, that equals more than a gallon of gasoline every day for each man, woman, and child.

27. How many Miles Do You Fly (both personal and or work) per month?

Previous Year	Monthly	For Year 2013

2014

INDIVIDUAL ENERGY USE EVALUATION CHART

To better understand your energy consumption and or energy footprint, please fill out the following form, estimated in monthly increments, then multiply the total(s) by 12 months. Estimations are acceptable for this purpose. However, the more accurate the estimations, the more accurate view of your energy use will be.

Personal Hygiene

1. Do you leave the water running while Brushing Your Teeth? (Y / N)

Brushing your teeth can use 1-2 gallons of water if left running, per brush.

2. How many Gallons of Water used running a shower/bath per month?
(Estimate how many hours per person, then add them together to get total)

Previous Year	Monthly	For Year 2014

The estimated cost to heat enough water for a 10 minute shower (15-30 gallons per shower) 30 times per month is $20.11.

3. How many times do you Flush the Toilet?
(Estimate on a monthly basis per person in household)

Previous Year	Monthly	For Year 2014

An average person uses about 123 gallons (466 liters) of water daily. Flushing the toilet can use up to 5-7 gallons per day.

Household

4. How many Light-bulbs Do You Use in your home?

Monthly	For Year 2012	For Year 2014

5. Fluorescent (Y / N) Incandescent (Y / N) Mixture of both (Y / N)

2014

6. How many hours are Lights Left In Use/On per month?

Previous Year | Monthly | For Year 2014

A typical incandescent light-bulb running 8 hours a day every day costs $18.25 per year while a florescent bulb running the same is $14.60. Multiply this total by the amount of bulbs in your in use within your house.

7. How many hours do you use the AC/Heat per month?

Previous Year | Monthly | For Year 2014

The average Central AC system (2.5 tons) can use 3500 watts per hour of continuous use. A medium sized window unit consumes 900 watts.

8. How many times do you Change Your Air Filter per month?

Previous Year | Monthly | For Year 2014

Changing your air filter frequently helps your heat and air systems run more efficiently, saving you money.

9. How many Batteries (AAA, AA, C, D, etc.) do you use in a month?

Previous Year | Monthly | For Year 2014

Depending on the size/wattage of the battery, costs for battery packages can range from $2.50 - $5+. Take into account the size and how many batteries you use for various use.

10. What is the monthly average of your Gas/Heating Oil Bill?

Previous Year | Monthly | For Year 2014

The average US Gas utility bill runs $20-$35 in the summer, and $100-200+ in the winter depending on the size of your house and the severity of the winter. It can be less than $100 if you have a small house where it doesn't get too cold.

2014

11. What is the monthly average of your Electric Bill?

Previous Year   Monthly   For Year 2014

The average US electric utility bill runs near $50-$75 in the summer, and $100-200+ in the winter depending on the size of your house and the severity of the winter. It can be less than $100 if you have a small house/apartment where it doesn't get too cold.

12. How many hours of Cooking with Gas/Electric do you do monthly?

Previous Year   Monthly   For Year 2014

13. How many Loads of Laundry do you do per month?

Previous Year   Monthly   For Year 2014

The average cost of doing 15 loads of laundry in a Hot/Warm Rinse cycle and ⊠ full dryer costs $16.16.

14. How many hours do you spend Doing Dishes?
(If running dishwasher, estimate time that it runs start to finish)

Previous Year   Monthly   For Year 2014

Running the average dishwasher for 15 loads per month (9-12 gallons per load) for a full cycle costs $19.15 per month.

15. How many pots of coffee do you brew per month?

Previous Year   Monthly   For Year 2014

The average coffee maker cost 2.6¢ per brew.

Entertainment

16. How many Hours of Television do you watch on a monthly basis?

Previous Year   Monthly   For Year 2014

A 40"-42" LCD on average costs $41 per year to run.

2014

---

17. How many Hours Do You Spend Online?

	Previous Year	Monthly	For Year 2014

Personal Computer and Monitor: [(120 Watts + 150 Watts) ☐ 4 hours/day ☐ 365 days/year] ÷ 1000 = 394 kWh ☐ 8.5 cents/kWh = $33.51/year

18. How often would you say that you Eat/Dine Out?
(Estimate time(s) per month)

	Previous Year	Monthly	For Year 2014

19. The times you Dine Out, how many are "Fast Food" establishments?

	Previous Year	Monthly	For Year 2014

The EPA estimates each person throws away around 10-15 pounds of food each week. Fast Food ads to this amount with packaging of food and drink items as well as bagging and other containers.

20. How Many Handheld Devices do you have/use?
(Includes Cell Phones, iPod/mp3 Player, iPad/Tablet, Etc.)

	Previous Year	Monthly	For Year 2014

21. How many Hours of Charging Handheld Devices per month?
(Estimate hours per device, then multiply by number of devices you have)

	Previous Year	Monthly	For Year 2014

22. How many hours do you talk on a Land-line Phone per month?

	Previous Year	Monthly	For Year 2014

135

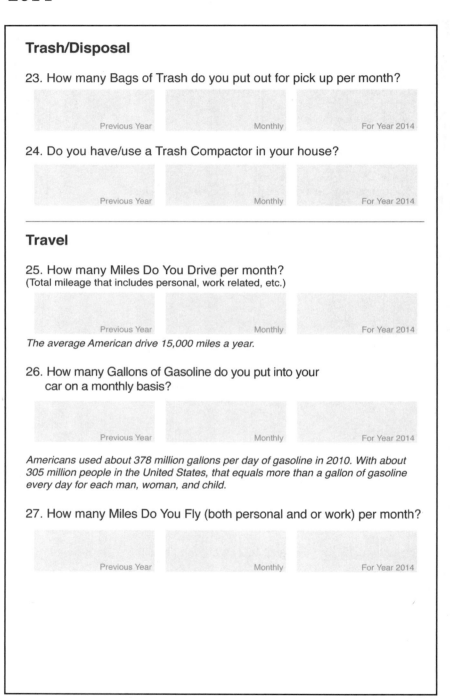

Trash/Disposal

23. How many Bags of Trash do you put out for pick up per month?

Previous Year   Monthly   For Year 2014

24. Do you have/use a Trash Compactor in your house?

Previous Year   Monthly   For Year 2014

Travel

25. How many Miles Do You Drive per month?
(Total mileage that includes personal, work related, etc.)

Previous Year   Monthly   For Year 2014

The average American drive 15,000 miles a year.

26. How many Gallons of Gasoline do you put into your
car on a monthly basis?

Previous Year   Monthly   For Year 2014

Americans used about 378 million gallons per day of gasoline in 2010. With about
305 million people in the United States, that equals more than a gallon of gasoline
every day for each man, woman, and child.

27. How many Miles Do You Fly (both personal and or work) per month?

Previous Year   Monthly   For Year 2014

2015

INDIVIDUAL ENERGY USE EVALUATION CHART

To better understand your energy consumption and or energy footprint, please fill out the following form, estimated in monthly increments, then multiply the total(s) by 12 months. Estimations are acceptable for this purpose. However, the more accurate the estimations, the more accurate view of your energy use will be.

Personal Hygiene

1. Do you leave the water running while Brushing Your Teeth? (Y / N)

Brushing your teeth can use 1-2 gallons of water if left running, per brush.

2. How many Gallons of Water used running a shower/bath per month?
(Estimate how many hours per person, then add them together to get total)

Previous Year	Monthly	For Year 2015

The estimated cost to heat enough water for a 10 minute shower (15-30 gallons per shower) 30 times per month is $20.11.

3. How many times do you Flush the Toilet?
(Estimate on a monthly basis per person in household)

Previous Year	Monthly	For Year 2015

An average person uses about 123 gallons (466 liters) of water daily. Flushing the toilet can use up to 5-7 gallons per day.

Household

4. How many Light-bulbs Do You Use in your home?

Monthly	For Year 2012	For Year 2015

5. Fluorescent (Y / N) Incandescent (Y / N) Mixture of both (Y / N)

6. How many hours are Lights Left In Use/On per month?

Previous Year	Monthly	For Year 2015

A typical incandescent light-bulb running 8 hours a day every day costs $18.25 per year while a florescent bulb running the same is $14.60. Multiply this total by the amount of bulbs in your in use within your house.

7. How many hours do you use the AC/Heat per month?

Previous Year	Monthly	For Year 2015

The average Central AC system (2.5 tons) can use 3500 watts per hour of continuous use. A medium sized window unit consumes 900 watts.

8. How many times do you Change Your Air Filter per month?

Previous Year	Monthly	For Year 2015

Changing your air filter frequently helps your heat and air systems run more efficiently, saving you money.

9. How many Batteries (AAA, AA, C, D, etc.) do you use in a month?

Previous Year	Monthly	For Year 2015

Depending on the size/wattage of the battery, costs for battery packages can range from $2.50 - $5+. Take into account the size and how many batteries you use for various use.

10. What is the monthly average of your Gas/Heating Oil Bill?

Previous Year	Monthly	For Year 2015

The average US Gas utility bill runs $20-$35 in the summer, and $100-200+ in the winter depending on the size of your house and the severity of the winter. It can be less than $100 if you have a small house where it doesn't get too cold.

2015

---

11. What is the monthly average of your Electric Bill?

Previous Year   Monthly   For Year 2015

The average US electric utility bill runs near $50-$75 in the summer, and $100-200+ in the winter depending on the size of your house and the severity of the winter. It can be less than $100 if you have a small house/apartment where it doesn't get too cold.

12. How many hours of Cooking with Gas/Electric do you do monthly?

Previous Year   Monthly   For Year 2015

13. How many Loads of Laundry do you do per month?

Previous Year   Monthly   For Year 2015

The average cost of doing 15 loads of laundry in a Hot/Warm Rinse cycle and ⊠ full dryer costs $16.16.

14. How many hours do you spend Doing Dishes?
(If running dishwasher, estimate time that it runs start to finish)

Previous Year   Monthly   For Year 2015

Running the average dishwasher for 15 loads per month (9-12 gallons per load) for a full cycle costs $19.15 per month.

15. How many pots of coffee do you brew per month?

Previous Year   Monthly   For Year 2015

The average coffee maker cost 2.6¢ per brew.

Entertainment

16. How many Hours of Television do you watch on a monthly basis?

Previous Year   Monthly   For Year 2015

A 40"-42" LCD on average costs $41 per year to run.

2015

17. How many Hours Do You Spend Online?

Previous Year	Monthly	For Year 2015

Personal Computer and Monitor: [(120 Watts + 150 Watts) ☐ 4 hours/day ☐ 365 days/year] ÷ 1000 = 394 kWh ☐ 8.5 cents/kWh = $33.51/year

18. How often would you say that you Eat/Dine Out?
(Estimate time(s) per month)

Previous Year	Monthly	For Year 2015

19. The times you Dine Out, how many are "Fast Food" establishments?

Previous Year	Monthly	For Year 2015

The EPA estimates each person throws away around 10-15 pounds of food each week. Fast Food ads to this amount with packaging of food and drink items as well as bagging and other containers.

20. How Many Handheld Devices do you have/use?
(Includes Cell Phones, iPod/mp3 Player, iPad/Tablet, Etc.)

Previous Year	Monthly	For Year 2015

21. How many Hours of Charging Handheld Devices per month?
(Estimate hours per device, then multiply by number of devices you have)

Previous Year	Monthly	For Year 2015

22. How many hours do you talk on a Land-line Phone per month?

Previous Year	Monthly	For Year 2015

2015

Trash/Disposal

23. How many Bags of Trash do you put out for pick up per month?

Previous Year   Monthly   For Year 2015

24. Do you have/use a Trash Compactor in your house?

Previous Year   Monthly   For Year 2015

Travel

25. How many Miles Do You Drive per month?
(Total mileage that includes personal, work related, etc.)

Previous Year   Monthly   For Year 2015

The average American drive 15,000 miles a year.

26. How many Gallons of Gasoline do you put into your
    car on a monthly basis?

Previous Year   Monthly   For Year 2015

Americans used about 378 million gallons per day of gasoline in 2010. With about 305 million people in the United States, that equals more than a gallon of gasoline every day for each man, woman, and child.

27. How many Miles Do You Fly (both personal and or work) per month?

Previous Year   Monthly   For Year 2015

2016

INDIVIDUAL ENERGY USE EVALUATION CHART

To better understand your energy consumption and or energy footprint, please fill out the following form, estimated in monthly increments, then multiply the total(s) by 12 months. Estimations are acceptable for this purpose. However, the more accurate the estimations, the more accurate view of your energy use will be.

Personal Hygiene

1. Do you leave the water running while Brushing Your Teeth? (Y / N)

Brushing your teeth can use 1-2 gallons of water if left running, per brush.

2. How many Gallons of Water used running a shower/bath per month?
(Estimate how many hours per person, then add them together to get total)

| Previous Year | Monthly | For Year 2016 |

The estimated cost to heat enough water for a 10 minute shower (15-30 gallons per shower) 30 times per month is $20.11.

3. How many times do you Flush the Toilet?
(Estimate on a monthly basis per person in household)

| Previous Year | Monthly | For Year 2016 |

An average person uses about 123 gallons (466 liters) of water daily. Flushing the toilet can use up to 5-7 gallons per day.

Household

4. How many Light-bulbs Do You Use in your home?

| Monthly | For Year 2012 | For Year 2016 |

5. Fluorescent (Y / N) Incandescent (Y / N) Mixture of both (Y / N)

2016

6. How many hours are Lights Left In Use/On per month?

| Previous Year | Monthly | For Year 2016 |

A typical incandescent light-bulb running 8 hours a day every day costs $18.25 per year while a florescent bulb running the same is $14.60. Multiply this total by the amount of bulbs in your in use within your house.

7. How many hours do you use the AC/Heat per month?

| Previous Year | Monthly | For Year 2016 |

The average Central AC system (2.5 tons) can use 3500 watts per hour of continuous use. A medium sized window unit consumes 900 watts.

8. How many times do you Change Your Air Filter per month?

| Previous Year | Monthly | For Year 2016 |

Changing your air filter frequently helps your heat and air systems run more efficiently, saving you money.

9. How many Batteries (AAA, AA, C, D, etc.) do you use in a month?

| Previous Year | Monthly | For Year 2016 |

Depending on the size/wattage of the battery, costs for battery packages can range from $2.50 - $5+. Take into account the size and how many batteries you use for various use.

10. What is the monthly average of your Gas/Heating Oil Bill?

| Previous Year | Monthly | For Year 2016 |

The average US Gas utility bill runs $20-$35 in the summer, and $100-200+ in the winter depending on the size of your house and the severity of the winter. It can be less than $100 if you have a small house where it doesn't get too cold.

2016

11. What is the monthly average of your Electric Bill?

Previous Year	Monthly	For Year 2016

The average US electric utility bill runs near $50-$75 in the summer, and $100-200+ in the winter depending on the size of your house and the severity of the winter. It can be less than $100 if you have a small house/apartment where it doesn't get too cold.

12. How many hours of Cooking with Gas/Electric do you do monthly?

Previous Year	Monthly	For Year 2016

13. How many Loads of Laundry do you do per month?

Previous Year	Monthly	For Year 2016

The average cost of doing 15 loads of laundry in a Hot/Warm Rinse cycle and ⊠ full dryer costs $16.16.

14. How many hours do you spend Doing Dishes?
(If running dishwasher, estimate time that it runs start to finish)

Previous Year	Monthly	For Year 2016

Running the average dishwasher for 15 loads per month (9-12 gallons per load) for a full cycle costs $19.15 per month.

15. How many pots of coffee do you brew per month?

Previous Year	Monthly	For Year 2016

The average coffee maker cost 2.6¢ per brew.

Entertainment

16. How many Hours of Television do you watch on a monthly basis?

Previous Year	Monthly	For Year 2016

A 40"-42" LCD on average costs $41 per year to run.

2016

17. How many Hours Do You Spend Online?

Previous Year	Monthly	For Year 2016

Personal Computer and Monitor: [(120 Watts + 150 Watts) ☐ 4 hours/day ☐ 365 days/year] ÷ 1000 = 394 kWh ☐ 8.5 cents/kWh = $33.51/year

18. How often would you say that you Eat/Dine Out?
(Estimate time(s) per month)

Previous Year	Monthly	For Year 2016

19. The times you Dine Out, how many are "Fast Food" establishments?

Previous Year	Monthly	For Year 2016

The EPA estimates each person throws away around 10-15 pounds of food each week. Fast Food ads to this amount with packaging of food and drink items as well as bagging and other containers.

20. How Many Handheld Devices do you have/use?
(Includes Cell Phones, iPod/mp3 Player, iPad/Tablet, Etc.)

Previous Year	Monthly	For Year 2016

21. How many Hours of Charging Handheld Devices per month?
(Estimate hours per device, then multiply by number of devices you have)

Previous Year	Monthly	For Year 2016

22. How many hours do you talk on a Land-line Phone per month?

Previous Year	Monthly	For Year 2016

2016

Trash/Disposal

23. How many Bags of Trash do you put out for pick up per month?

Previous Year   Monthly   For Year 2016

24. Do you have/use a Trash Compactor in your house?

Previous Year   Monthly   For Year 2016

Travel

25. How many Miles Do You Drive per month?
(Total mileage that includes personal, work related, etc.)

Previous Year   Monthly   For Year 2016

The average American drive 15,000 miles a year.

26. How many Gallons of Gasoline do you put into your
    car on a monthly basis?

Previous Year   Monthly   For Year 2016

Americans used about 378 million gallons per day of gasoline in 2010. With about 305 million people in the United States, that equals more than a gallon of gasoline every day for each man, woman, and child.

27. How many Miles Do You Fly (both personal and or work) per month?

Previous Year   Monthly   For Year 2016

Energy Industry Links

American Exploration & Production Council: www.AXPC.us

The Association of Energy Service Companies: www.AESC.net

CNG Now: www.CNGNow.com/Pages/information.aspx

Colorado Oil & Gas Association: www.COGA.org

The Energy Advocates: www.EnergyAdvocates.org

Independent Petroleum Association of America: www.IPAA.org

Independent Petroleum Association of New Mexico:
    www.IPANM.org

International Energy Policy Conference (IEPC):
    www.EnergyPolicyConference.com

Louisiana Oil & Gas Association: www.LOGA.la

Montana Petroleum Association: www.MontanaPetroleum.org

National Association of Royalty Owners (NARO):
    www.NARO-US.org

National Petroleum Council (NPC): www.NPC.org

National Stripper Well Association: www.NSWA.us

Oklahoma Independent Petroleum Association (OIPA):
    www.OIPA.com

Panhandle Producers & Royalty Owners Association:
    www.PPROA.org

Pennsylvania Independent Oil & Gas Association: www.PIOGA.org

Petroleum Equipment Suppliers Association: www.PESA.org

Petroleum Technology Transfer Council: www.PTTC.org

Pickens Plan: www.PickensPlan.com/act/

The Stripper Well Consortium: www.Energy.PSU.edu/swc

Texas Alliance of Energy Producers: www.TexasAlliance.org

US Department of Energy: www.Energy.gov

US Energy Information Administration (EIA): www.EIA.gov

Western Energy Alliance: www.WesternEnergyAlliance.org

Midland-Reporter Telegram Article

Special to the Oil Report
By Paul Wiseman

Other than Wall Street, few other segments of the economy attract as much vitriol as the energy industry in general and oil and gas in particular.

Realizing that just as much energy must be expended to clean up its public image as is spent on cleaning up an oil spill, spokesman Mark Stansberry of Oklahoma-based Energy Advocates is going on the road in 2012 to both disburse and collect information. Energy Advocates is a nonprofit group founded in 1974 to promote oil, gas, coal, wind, solar and other forms of energy to the general public. A former president of EA (2003-2009), Stansberry is also chairman of the GTD Group, an energy investment and trade company with a focus on natural gas.

"What we're trying to do is to get out more and have more hands-on talks with folks . . . in different cities, making speeches and hosting round-tables, conferences, whatever, especially in 2012," said Stansberry. "We want to find out what's on the minds of people" regarding energy. The fact that 2012 is an election year means public policy will be more on peoples' minds, but Stansberry said that was not the primary reason for scheduling a tour in that time frame.

"It's more like, the message doesn't seem to be—as far as energy education—reaching everyone," he said. His goal is to raise public awareness of the need for energy and that energy is not a bad thing. "Really, energy is our friend—nothing moves without energy," he pointed out, listing agriculture, transportation and health care among other sectors that depend greatly on energy for their own survival.

Because Energy Advocates involves all major types of energy, part of the city-to-city discussions will involve how to best use each type, and to use all types efficiently. The discussion also will involve questions of who should make those decisions—should they be left to consumers or should government get involved, especially to promote such things as wind and solar energy that do not currently compete with oil and gas on an economic basis—and should oil and gas be taxed to pay for those subsidies?

As a supporter of natural gas himself, Stansberry noted even that fuel could need government support to gain more use. Because natural gas is cleaner burning than gasoline or diesel and because the US does not import the fuel as it does crude oil, some have advocated using natural gas in vehicles. Doing so, however, would involve a huge investment in infrastructure to deliver natural gas to fueling stations across the country. Stansberry compared the possibility of government support for such a task to its investment in the interstate highway system. "Sometimes a partnership does occur between government and private enterprise," he said, adding that, ultimately, the market should drive the demand.

On the tour Stansberry will seek out community leaders in economic development, media, legislators as well as consumers, in groups of five to seven people. Some roundtables will involve twenty or more attendees. "We'll get a dialogue going as to what people would like to see in their area, what we can do to assist in the education effort. I can see us assisting, especially in the Panhandle and in your area on the wind energy side," he explained. "What we've done successfully is to share the pros and cons (about various forms of energy) and to let the people decide.

As an example of what to expect, Stansberry recalled a recent round table in Kansas City involving twenty or so community leaders. He asked the participants about their perceptions of various fuels. Of coal, the perception was that it is "very dirty." Of natural gas, they said, "We hear it's clean."

"I got to one question I thought was really interesting—I asked them what they thought of the Pickens plan. I asked if they had signed up or if they knew about it. And roughly two out of ten had even heard of it," he said.

The Pickens Plan, named for its author, oilman T. Boone Pickens, who came forward with the plan in the summer of 2008, proposes the building of thousands of wind generation farms which, in his view, would provide 20 percent of US electricity needs. The natural gas that would have been required to generate that power could then be funneled into vehicle use, reducing the need for imported oil by 38 percent, according to his figures.

Perhaps the most informative meeting was one held in Washington, DC, with college students from that city. "They told us, 'You're approaching it all wrong' in education. They said that we should be doing more of the social media instead of print." One idea was to do videos on YouTube. The students referred to a video on that site promoting clean coal, which apparently had convinced several of them on that topic. For that age group, Stansberry said, "We probably are approaching it all wrong."

In the realm of public image, he admitted, each type of energy has its cons. For natural gas, it is hydraulic fracturing, for nuclear energy it is the waste, for coal it is miner safety and air quality, for wind the concerns are about safety for birds flying nearby, solar was hurt by the Solyndra scandal and so on. There is dispute over whether some of those issues are overstated, but the perceptions still affect public opinion.

If the public became better educated on the issues for each type of energy they could make decisions on the facts rather than on sound bites—then they could inform legislators of what they want,

Stansberry said. In his own quest to educate the public, Stansberry said he does not have a firm count of the number of stops he plans to make, choosing to see what opportunities arise.

Reprinted from the Midland-Reporter Telegram, *December 11, 2011*

Recommended Reading

A Simple Government. Mike Huckabee. Sentinel.

A Strategy for American Power: Energy, Climate and National Security. Sharon Burke and Christine Parthemore. Contributing Authors: Josh Busby, Christine Matthews, Amy Myers Jaffe, Jason Furman. Center for a New American Security.

A Thousand Barrels a Second: The Coming Oil Break Point and the Challenges Facing an Energy Dependent World. Peter Tertzakian. McGraw Hill.

Beyond Oil: The View from Hubbert's Peak. Kenneth S. Deffeyes. Hill and Wang.

Blood and Oil: The Dangers and Consequences of America's Growing Dependency on Imported Petroleum. Michael T. Klare. Metropolitan Books, Henry Holt and Company.

Drill Here, Drill Now, Pay Less: A Handbook For Slashing Gas Prices and Solving Our Energy Crisis. Former Speaker Newt Gingrich. Regenery Publishing Inc.

Freedom from Oil: How The Next President Can End The United State's Oil Addiction. David Sandalow. McGraw Hill.

Future Energy: How the New Oil Industry Will Change People, Politics, and Portfolios. Bill Paul. John Wiley & Son Inc.

Global Energy Innovation. Woodrow W. Clark II, PhD, and Grant Cooke. Praeger Press, 2011.

Global Warming: Understanding the Forecast. Andrew Revkin. Abbeyville Press Publishers, New York.

Hydrogen as a Future Energy Carrier. Andreas Zuttel. Andreas Borgschulte and Louis Schlapbach, Editors. John Wiley & Sons Inc.

Money in The Ground. John Orban III. Meridian Press.

Oil on the Brain: Petroleum's Long, Strange Trip to Your Tank. Lisa Margonelli. Broadway Publishing.

Oil Power: The Rise and Imminent Fall of an American Empire. Carl Solberg. A Mentor Book, New American Library.

Oil Property Evaluation. John M. Campbell. Prentice-Hall Inc.

Out of Gas: The End of the Age of Oil. David Goodstein. W. W. Norton and Company, New York.

Over a Barrel: A Simple Guide to the Oil Shortage. Tom Mast. Hayden Publishers.

Power from the Earth. Thomas Gold. J. M. Dent & Sons Ltd., London.

Scientific American: July 2009. Scientific American Inc.

Sustainable Communities Design Handbook. Woodrow W. Clark II, PhD. Elsevier Press, 2010.

Sustaining Security: How Natural Resources Influence National Security. Christine Parthemore with Will Rogers. Center for a New American Security.

The Rough Guide to the Energy Crisis. David Buchan. Penguin.

The Secret of Sherwood Forest: Oil Production in England During World War II. Guy H. Woodward and Grace Steele Woodward. University of Oklahoma Press, Norman.

The Bottomless Well: The Twilight of Fuel, The Virtue of Waste, and Why We Will Never Run Out of Energy. Peter Huber and Mark Mills. Basic Books, Terseus Books Group, New York.

The Braking Point: America's Energy Dreams and Global Economic Realities. Mark A. Stansberry with Jason Reimbold. Hawk Publishing Group.

The End of Oil: On the Edge of a Perilous New World. Paul Roberts. Mariner Books, Houghton Mifflin Company.

The GET: Grand Energy Transition. Robert A. Hefner III. Hefner Foundation.

The Hydrogen Age: Empowering a Clean-Energy Future. Geoffrey Holland and James Provenzano. Gibbs Smith Publishing.

The Hydrogen Economy. Jeremy Rifkin. Jeremy P. Tarcher/Penguin, Penguin Group.

The New Great Game: Blood and Oil In Central Asia. Lutz Kleveman. Atlantic Monthly Press.

The Oil Factor: Protect Yourself and Profit from the Coming Energy Crisis. Stephen Leeb and Donna Leeb. Warner Business Books.

The Oklahoma Petroleum Industry. Kenny A. Franks. University of Oklahoma Press, Norman.

The Prize: The Epic Quest for Oil, Money & Power. Daniel Yergin. Free Press Simon & Schuster.

The Tyranny of Oil: The World's Most Powerful Industry and What We Must Do To Stop It. Antonia Juhasz. William Morrow.

The Quest: Energy, Security, and the Remaking of the Modern World. Daniel Yergin. Penguin Press.

Tomorrow's Energy: Hydrogen Fuel Cells, and the Prospects for a Cleaner Planet. Peter Hoffman. MIT Press.

Twilight in the Desert: The Coming Saudi Oil Shock and the World Economy. Matthew R. Simmons. John Wiley & Sons Inc.

Petroleum-Based Consumer Products

How many products do we use in our daily lives that are petroleum-based? The answer is a great many. The following list includes some of the more recognized items:

- air conditioners
- ammonia
- anesthetics
- antifreeze
- antihistamines
- antiseptics
- artificial limbs
- artificial turf
- asphalt
- aspirin
- awnings
- balloons
- ballpoint pens
- bandages
- basketballs
- bearing grease
- bicycle tires
- boats
- bottles
- bras
- bubble gum
- butane
- cameras
- candles
- car battery cases
- car bodies
- car enamel
- carpet
- cassette tapes
- caulking
- CD players
- CDs
- chewing gum
- clothes
- clotheslines
- cold cream
- combs and brushes
- computers
- contacts
- cortisone
- crayons
- cream
- curtains
- dashboards
- denture adhesive
- dentures
- deodorant
- detergents
- dice
- diesel
- dishes
- dishwasher

- dishwashing liquid
- dresses
- drinking cups
- dryers
- dyes
- electric blankets
- electrician's tape
- enamel
- epoxy
- eyeglasses
- fan belts
- faucet washers
- fertilizers
- fishing boots
- fishing lures
- fishing rods
- floor wax
- folding doors
- food preservatives
- football cleats
- football helmets
- footballs
- gasoline
- glues
- glycerin
- golf bags
- golf balls
- guitar strings
- hair coloring
- hearing aids
- hair curlers
- hand lotion
- heart valves
- heating oil
- house paint
- ice chests
- ice cube trays
- ink
- insect repellent
- insecticides
- insulation
- jet fuel
- life jackets
- linings
- linoleum
- lip balm
- lipstick
- loudspeakers
- luggage
- medicines
- model cars
- mops
- motor oil
- motorcycle helmets
- movie film
- nail polish
- nylon rope
- oil filters
- paddles
- paint
- paint brushes
- paint rollers
- panty hose
- parachutes
- paraffin
- pens
- percolators
- perfumes
- petroleum jelly
- pillows
- plastics
- plastic wood

- plastic chairs
- plastic cups
- plastic forks
- plastic wrap
- plywood adhesives
- purses
- putty
- refrigerant
- refrigerators
- roller-skate wheels
- roofing paper
- rubber bands
- rubber boots
- rubber cement
- rubbing alcohol
- running shoes
- saccharine
- safety glasses
- seals
- shag rugs
- shampoo
- shaving cream
- shirts (non-cotton)
- shoe polish
- shoes
- shower curtains
- skis
- slacks
- soap
- soft contact lenses
- solvents
- speakers
- sports car bodies
- stereos
- sunglasses
- surfboards

- sweaters
- synthetic rubber
- table tennis balls
- tape recorders
- telephones
- tennis rackets
- tents
- thermos
- tights
- tires
- toilet seats
- toners
- toolboxes
- tool racks
- toothbrushes
- toothpaste
- transparencies
- transparent tape
- trash bags
- TV cabinets
- typewriter and computer ribbons
- tires
- umbrellas
- upholstery
- vaporizers
- vitamin capsules
- volleyballs
- water pipes
- water skis
- wax
- wax paper
- wheels
- yarn

Glossary

#

3-D Seismic: A relatively new exploration technique used in the search for oil and gas in underground structures. The basic premise behind seismic is the same as ultrasound technology used in the medical field. Sound from a shot hole is recorded from geophones and interpreted to give a picture of the underlying structures within the earth. This has now become a common practice to redefine and identify known as well as unknown structures. Many times these structures contain traps that hold oil and gas yet to be discovered.

4-D Seismic: The newest advances in seismic technology now take into consideration a fourth dimension: time. With 4-D seismic, geologists are able to monitor the movement and mobility of oil as it is extracted in the petroleum process.

A

Acid rain: Also called acid precipitation or acid deposition, acid rain is precipitation containing harmful amounts of nitric and sulfuric acids formed primarily by sulfur dioxide and nitrogen oxides released into the atmosphere when fossil fuels are burned. It can be wet precipitation (rain, snow, or fog) or dry precipitation (absorbed gaseous and particulate matter, aerosol particles, or dust). Acid rain has a pH below 5.6. Normal rain has a pH of about 5.6, which is slightly acidic. The term "pH" is a measure of acidity or alkalinity and ranges from 0 to 14. A pH measurement of 7 is regarded as neutral. Measurements below 7 indicate increased acidity, while those above 7 indicate increased alkalinity.

Acre-foot: The volume of water that will cover an area of one acre to a depth of one foot.

Acreage: An area measured in acres that is subject to ownership or control by those holding total or fractional shares of working interests. Acreage is considered developed when development has been completed. A distinction may be made between "gross" acreage and "net" acreage:

- Gross—All acreage covered by any working interest, regardless of the percentage of ownership in the interest.
- Net—Gross acreage adjusted to reflect the percentage of ownership in the working interest in the acreage.

Active power: The component of electric power that performs work, typically measured in kilowatts (kW) or megawatts (MW). Also known as real power. The terms "active" or "real" are used to modify the base term "power" to differentiate it from reactive power.

Active solar: As an energy source, energy from the sun collected and stored using mechanical pumps or fans to circulate heat-laden fluids or air between solar collectors and a building.

Actual peak reduction: The actual reduction in annual peak load (measured in kilowatts) achieved by customers who participate in a utility demand-side management (DSM) program. It reflects changes in the demand for electricity resulting from a utility DSM program that is in effect at the same time the utility experiences its annual peak load, as opposed to the installed peak load reduction capability (i.e., potential peak reduction). It should account for the regular cycling of energy efficient units during the period of annual peak load.

Adequacy (electric): The ability of the electric system to supply the aggregate electrical demand and energy requirements of end-use customers at all times, taking into account scheduled and reasonably expected unscheduled outages of system elements.

Aftermarket converted vehicle: A standard, conventionally fueled, factory-produced vehicle to which equipment has been added that enables the vehicle to operate on alternative fuel.

Aftermarket vehicle converter: An organization or individual that modifies OEM vehicles after first use or sale to operate on a different fuel (or fuels).

AFV (alternative-fuel vehicle): A vehicle designed to operate on an alternative fuel (e.g., compressed natural gas, methane blend, electricity). The vehicle could be either a dedicated vehicle designed to operate exclusively on alternative fuel or a non-dedicated vehicle designed to operate on alternative fuel and traditional fuel alternately.

Agglomerating character: Agglomeration describes the caking properties of coal. Agglomerating character is determined by examination and testing of the residue when a small powdered sample is heated to 950°C under specific conditions. If the sample is "agglomerating," the residue will be coherent, show swelling or cell structure, and be capable of supporting a 500-gram weight without pulverizing.

Aggregate ratio: The ratio of two population aggregates (totals). For example, the aggregate expenditures per household is the ratio of the total expenditures in each category to the total number of households in the category.

Alkylate: The product of an alkylation reaction. It usually refers to the high-octane product from alkylation units. This alkylate is used in blending high octane gasoline.

Alkylation: A refining process for chemically combining isobutane with olefin hydrocarbons (e.g., propylene, butylene) through the control of temperature and pressure in the presence of an acid catalyst, usually sulfuric acid or hydrofluoric acid. The product alkylate, an isoparaffin, has high octane value and is blended with motor and aviation gasoline to improve the antiknock value of the fuel.

Alternative fuel: Alternative fuel, for transportation applications include the following:

- methanol
- denatured ethanol and other alcohols
- fuel mixtures containing 85 percent or more by volume of methanol, denatured ethanol, and other alcohols with gasoline or other fuels
- natural gas
- liquefied petroleum gas (propane)
- hydrogen
- coal-derived liquid fuels
- fuels (other than alcohol) derived from biological materials, e.g., biofuels such as soy diesel fuels
- electricity (including electricity from solar energy)

"Any other fuel the Secretary determines, by rule, is substantially not petroleum and would yield substantial energy security benefits and substantial environmental benefits." The term "alternative fuel" does not include alcohol or other blended portions of primarily petroleum-based fuels used as oxygenates or extenders, i.e., MTBE, ETBE, other ethers, and the 10 percent ethanol portion of gasohol.

ANSI: American National Standards Institute.

ANSI assembly identifier: The serial numbering scheme adopted by the American National Standards Institute (ANSI) to ensure the uniqueness of an assembly serial number.

Anthracite: The highest rank of coal; used primarily for residential and commercial space heating. It is a hard, brittle, and black lustrous coal, often referred to as hard coal, containing a high percentage of fixed carbon and a low percentage of volatile matter. The moisture content of fresh-mined anthracite generally is less than 15 percent. The heat content of anthracite ranges from twenty-two to twenty-eight million Btu per ton on a moist, mineral-matter-free basis. The heat content of anthracite coal consumed in the United States averages twenty-five million Btu per ton on the as-received basis (i.e., containing both inherent moisture and mineral matter). **Note:** Since the 1980s, anthracite refuse or mine waste has been used for steam electric power generation. This fuel typically has a heat content of fifteen million Btu per ton or less.

Anticline: A geological term describing a fold in the earth's surface with strata sloping downward on both sides from a common crest. Anticlines frequently have surface manifestations like hills, knobs, and ridges. At least 80 percent of the world's oil and gas has been found in anticlines.

API: American Petroleum Institute, a trade association.

API gravity: American Petroleum Institute's measure of specific gravity of crude oil or condensate in degrees. An arbitrary scale expressing the gravity or density of liquid petroleum products. The measuring scale is calibrated in terms of degrees API; it is calculated as follows:

$$\text{Degrees API} = (141.5 \, / \, \text{sp. gr. } 60°\text{F} \, / \, 60°\text{F}) - 131.5$$

Assistance for heating in winter: Assistance from the Low-Income Home Energy Assistance Program (LIHEAP). The purpose of LIHEAP is to assist eligible households to meet the costs of home energy, i.e., a source of heating or cooling residential buildings.

Assistance for weatherization of residence: The household received services free, or at a reduced cost, from the federal, state, or local government. Any of the following services could have been received: insulation in the attic, outside wall, basement, or crawlspace below the floor of the house; insulation around the hot water heater; repair of broken windows or doors to keep out the cold or hot weather; weather stripping or caulking around any windows or doors to the outside;

storm doors or windows added; repair of broken furnace; furnace tune-up and modifications; other home energy-saving devices.

Average daily production: The ratio of the total production at a mining operation to the total number of production days worked at the operation.

Average delivered price: The weighted average of all contract price commitments and market price settlements in a delivery year.

B

Backup fuel: In a central heat pump system, the fuel used in the furnace that takes over the space heating when the outdoor temperature drops below that feasible to operate a heat pump.

Backup generator: A generator that is used only for test purposes or in the event of an emergency, such as a shortage of power needed to meet customer load requirements.

Barrel: A unit of volume equal to forty-two US gallons.

Base load: The minimum amount of electric power delivered or required over a given period of time at a steady rate.

Base load capacity: The generating equipment normally operated to serve loads on an around-the-clock basis.

Base load plant: A plant, usually housing high-efficiency steam-electric units, which is normally operated to take all or part of the minimum load of a system and consequently produces electricity at an essentially constant rate and runs continuously. These units are operated to maximize system mechanical and thermal efficiency and minimize system operating costs.

bbl: The abbreviation for barrel(s).

bbl/d: The abbreviation for barrel(s) per day.

bbl/sd: The abbreviation for barrel(s) per steam day.

BCF: The abbreviation for billion cubic feet. The cubic foot is a standard unit of measure for gas at atmospheric pressure.

Benzene (C_6H_6): An aromatic hydrocarbon present in small proportion in some crude oils and made commercially from petroleum by the catalytic reforming of naphthenes in petroleum naphtha. Also made from coal in the manufacturing of coke. Used as a solvent in the manufacturing of detergents, synthetic fibers, petrochemicals, and as a component of high-octane gasoline.

Biobutanol: Butanol ($C_4H_{10}O$) or butyl alcohol is an alcohol that can be used as a solvent or fuel. Biobutanol refers to butanol that has been produced from biomass.

Biodiesel: A fuel typically made from soybean, canola, or other vegetable oils; animal fats; and recycled grease. It can serve as a substitute for petroleum-derived diesel or distillate fuel. For EIA reporting, it is a fuel composed of mono-alkyl esters of long chain fatty acids derived from vegetable oils or animal fats, designated B100, and meeting the requirements of ASTM (American Society for Testing Materials) D6751.

Biofuels: Liquid fuels and blending components produced from biomass feedstocks, used primarily for transportation.

Biogenic: Produced by biological processes of living organisms. **Note:** EIA uses the term "biogenic" to refer only to organic non-fossil material of biological origin.

Biomass: Any organic material, such as wood, plants, and organic wastes, which can be turned into fuel.

Bitumen: A naturally occurring viscous mixture, mainly of hydrocarbons heavier than pentane, that may contain sulphur compounds and that, in its natural occurring viscous state, is not recoverable at a commercial rate through a well.

Bituminous coal: A dense coal, usually black, sometimes dark brown, often with well-defined bands of bright and dull material, used primarily as fuel in steam-electric power generation, with substantial quantities also used for heat and power applications in manufacturing, and to make coke. Bituminous coal is the most abundant coal in active US mining regions. Its moisture content usually is less than 20 percent. The heat content of bituminous coal ranges from twenty-one to thirty million Btu per ton on a moist, mineral-matter-free basis. The heat content of bituminous coal consumed in the United States averages twenty-four million Btu per ton, on the as-received basis (i.e., containing both inherent moisture and mineral matter).

BOE: Barrels of oil equivalent (used internationally).

Breeder reactor: A reactor that both produces and consumes fissionable fuel, especially one that creates more fuel than it consumes. The new fissionable material is created by a process known as breeding, in which neutrons from fission are captured in fertile materials.

Btu (British thermal unit): A standard measure of heat content in a fuel. One Btu equals the amount of energy required to raise the temperature of one pound of water 1°F at or near 39.2°F.

Btu conversion factor: A factor for converting energy data between one unit of measurement and British thermal units (Btu). Btu conversion factors are generally used to convert energy data from physical units of measure (such as barrels, cubic feet, or short tons) into the energy-equivalent measure of Btu.

Btu per cubic foot: The total heating value, expressed in Btu, produced by the combustion, at constant pressure, of the amount of the gas that would occupy a volume of one cubic foot at a temperature of 60°F if saturated with water vapor and under a pressure equivalent to that of thirty inches of mercury at 32°F and under standard gravitational force (980.665 cm. per sec. squared) with air of the same temperature and pressure as the gas, when the products of combustion are cooled to the initial temperature of gas and air when the water formed by combustion is condensed to the liquid state. Sometimes called gross heating value or total heating value.

Bundled utility service (electric): A means of operation whereby energy, transmission, and distribution services, as well as ancillary and retail services, are provided by one entity.

Burn days: The number of days the station could continue to operate by burning coal already on hand assuming no additional deliveries of coal and an average consumption rate.

Butane (C_4H_{10}): A normally gaseous straight-chain or branch-chain hydrocarbon extracted from hydrocarbon extracted from natural gas or refinery gas streams. It includes isobutane and normal butane and is designated in ASTM Specification D1835 and Gas Processors Association Specifications for commercial butane.

Butanol ($C_4H_{10}O$): (Or butyl alcohol) an alcohol that can be used as a solvent or fuel.

Butylene (C_4H_8): An olefinic hydrocarbon recovered from refinery processes.

C

CAFE: Corporate average fuel economy.

Carbon dioxide (CO_2): A colorless, odorless, non-poisonous gas that is a normal part of Earth's atmosphere. Carbon dioxide is a product of fossil-fuel combustion as well as other processes. It is considered a greenhouse gas as it traps heat (infrared energy) radiated by the earth into the atmosphere and thereby contributes to the potential for global warming. The global warming potential (GWP) of other greenhouse gases is measured in relation to that of carbon dioxide, which by international scientific convention is assigned a value of one.

Carbon sequestration: The fixation of atmospheric carbon dioxide in a carbon sink through biological or physical processes.

Casinghead gas (or oil well gas): Natural gas produced along with crude oil from oil wells. It contains either dissolved or associated gas or both.

Catalyst coke: In many catalytic operations (e.g., catalytic cracking), carbon is deposited on the catalyst, thus deactivating the catalyst. The catalyst is reactivated by burning off the carbon, which is used as a fuel in the refining process. This carbon or coke is not recoverable in a concentrated form.

Catalytic converter: A device containing a catalyst for converting automobile exhaust into mostly harmless products.

Catalytic cracking: The refining process of breaking down the larger, heavier, and more complex hydrocarbon molecules into simpler and lighter molecules. Catalytic cracking is accomplished by the use of a catalytic agent and is an effective process for increasing the yield of gasoline from crude oil. Catalytic cracking processes fresh feeds and recycled feeds.

CERCLA: Comprehensive Environmental Response, Compensation, and Liability Act.

CF: Cubic foot.

CH$_4$: Methane.

Chlorofluorocarbon (CFC): Any of various compounds consisting of carbon, hydrogen, chlorine, and flourine used as refrigerants. CFCs are now thought to be harmful to the earth's atmosphere.

CHP: Combined heat and power.

Christmas tree: An assembly of valves, gauges, and chokes mounted on a well casing head to control production and the flow of oil to pipelines.

Citygate: A point or measuring station at which a distributing gas utility receives gas from a natural gas pipeline company or transmission system.

CIV: Customs import value.

Climate change: A term used to refer to all forms of climatic inconsistency, but especially to significant changes from one prevailing climatic condition to another. In some cases, "climate change" has been used synonymously with the term "global warming"; scientists, however, tend to use the term in a wider sense inclusive of natural changes in climate, including climatic cooling.

CMSA: Consolidated metropolitan statistical area.

CNG: Compressed natural gas.

CO: Carbon monoxide.

CO_2: Carbon dioxide

CO_2 injection: A secondary recovery technique in which carbon dioxide (CO_2) is injected into wells as part of a miscible recovery program.

Coal: A readily combustible black or brownish-black rock whose composition, including inherent moisture, consists of more than 50 percent by weight and more than 70 percent by volume of carbonaceous material. It is formed from plant remains that have been compacted, hardened, chemically altered, and metamorphosed by heat and pressure over geologic time.

Coal bed: A bed or stratum of coal. Also called a coal seam.

Coal bed degasification: This refers to the removal of methane or coal bed gas from a coal mine before or during mining.

Coal bed methane: Methane is generated during coal formation and is contained in the coal microstructure. Typical recovery entails pumping water out of the coal to allow the gas to escape. Methane is the principal component of natural gas. Coal bed methane can be added to natural gas pipelines without any special treatment.

Coal gasification: The process of converting coal into gas. The basic process involves crushing coal to a powder, which is then heated in the presence of steam and oxygen to produce a gas. The gas is then refined to reduce sulfur and other impurities. The gas can be used as a fuel or processed further and concentrated into chemical or liquid fuel.

Coal liquefaction: A chemical process that converts coal into clean-burning liquid hydrocarbons, such as synthetic crude oil and methanol.

Cogeneration: The production of electrical energy and another form of useful energy (such as heat or steam) through the sequential use of energy.

Cogeneration system: A system using a common energy source to produce both electricity and steam for other uses, resulting in increased fuel efficiency.

Cogenerator: A generating facility that produces electricity and another form of useful thermal energy (such as heat or steam), used for industrial, commercial, heating, or cooling purposes. To receive status as a qualifying facility (QF) under the Public Utility Regulatory Policies Act (PURPA), the facility must produce electric energy and "another form of useful thermal energy through the sequential use of energy" and meet certain ownership, operating, and efficiency criteria established by the Federal Energy Regulatory Commission (FERC). (See the Code of Federal Regulations, Title 18, Part 292.)

Coke (coal): A solid carbonaceous residue derived from low-ash, low-sulfur bituminous coal from which the volatile constituents are driven off by baking in an oven at temperatures as high as 2,000° F so that the fixed carbon and residual ash are fused together. Coke is used as a fuel and as a reducing agent in smelting iron ore in a blast furnace. Coke from coal is grey, hard, and porous, and has a heating value of 24.8 million Btu per ton.

Coke (petroleum): A residue high in carbon content and low in hydrogen that is the final product of thermal decomposition in the condensation process in cracking. This product is reported as marketable coke or catalyst coke. The conversion is 5 barrels (of 42 US gallons each) per short ton. Coke from petroleum has a heating value of 6.024 million Btu per barrel.

Commingling: The mixing of one utility's generated supply of electric energy with another utility's generated supply within a transmission system.

Completed well, or completion (oil and gas production): The term refers to the installation of permanent equipment for the production of oil or gas. If a well is equipped to produce only oil or gas from one zone or reservoir, the definition of a "well" (classified as an oil well or gas well) and the definition of a "completion" are identical. However, if a well is equipped to produce oil or gas separately from more than one reservoir, a "well" is not synonymous with a "completion."

Compressed natural gas (CNG): Natural gas compressed to a pressure at or above 200–248 bar (i.e., 2900–3600 pounds per square inch) and stored in high-pressure containers. It is used as a fuel for natural gas-powered vehicles.

Concession: The operating right to explore for and develop petroleum fields in consideration for a share of production in kind (equity oil).

Conventional energy sources: Oil, gas, coal, and sometimes nuclear energy, in contrast to alternative energy sources such as solar, hydroelectric and geothermal power, synfuels, and biomass.

Conversion factor: A factor for converting data between one unit of measurement and another (such as between short tons and British thermal units, or between barrels and gallons).

Converted (alternative-fuel) vehicle: A vehicle originally designed to operate on gasoline or diesel that was modified or altered to run on an alternative fuel after its initial delivery to an end-user.

CPI: Consumer price index.

Cracking: The process of breaking down the larger, heavier, and more complex hydrocarbon molecules into simpler and lighter molecules, thus increasing the gasoline from crude oil. Cracking is done by application of heat and pressure, and in modern times the use of a catalytic agent.

Crude oil: Liquid petroleum as it comes out of the ground. Crude oils range from very light (high in gasoline) to very heavy (high in residual oils). Sour crude is high in sulfur content. Sweet crude is low in sulfur content and therefore is often more valuable.

Crude oil equivalent: A measure of energy content that converts units of different kinds of energy into the energy equivalent of barrels of oil.

Cubic foot (cf), natural gas: The amount of natural gas contained at standard temperature and pressure (60°F and 14.73 pounds standard per square inch) in a cube whose edges are one foot long.

D

Decatherm: Ten therms or 1,000,000 Btu.

Decommissioning: Retirement of a nuclear facility, including decontamination or dismantlement.

Deferred income tax (liability): A liability in the balance sheet representing the additional federal income taxes that would have been due if a utility had not been allowed to compute tax expenses differently for income tax reporting purposes than for ratemaking purposes.

Deforestation: The net removal of trees from forested land.

Degasification system: The methods employed for removing methane from a coal seam that could not otherwise be removed by standard ventilation fans, and thus would pose a substantial hazard to coal miners. These systems may be used prior to mining or during mining activities.

Delivered (gas): The physical transfer of natural, synthetic, or supplemental gas from facilities operated by the responding company to facilities operated by others or to consumers.

Delivered cost: The cost of fuel, including the invoice price of fuel, transportation charges, taxes, commissions, insurance, and expenses associated with leased or owned equipment used to transport the fuel.

Delivered energy: The amount of energy delivered to the site (building); no adjustment is made for the fuels consumed to produce electricity or district sources. This is also referred to as net energy.

Deliveries (electric): Energy generated by one system and delivered to another system through one or more transmission lines.

Demand: The requirement of energy needed to provide goods and services.

Demand destruction: The reduction of demand for a commodity due to the result of high prices.

Depletion allowance: A term for either 1) a periodic assignment to expense of recorded amounts or 2) an allowable income tax deduction that is related to the exhaustion of mineral reserves. Depletion is included as one of the elements of amortization. When used in that manner, depletion refers only to book depletion.

Diesel oil: A petroleum fraction composed primarily of aliphatic (linear or unbranched) hydrocarbons. Diesel is slightly heavier than kerosene.

Directional drilling: Drilling at an angle, instead of on the perpendicular, by using a whip stock to bend the pipe until it is going in the desired direction. Directional drilling is used to develop offshore leases, where it is very costly and sometimes impossible to prepare separate sites for every well; to reach oil beneath a building or some other location which cannot be drilled directly; or to control damage or as a last resort when a well has cratered. It is much more expensive than conventional drilling procedures.

Distillate: Liquid hydrocarbons, usually colorless and of high API gravity, recovered from wet gas by a separator that condenses the liquid out of the gas. The present term is natural gas.

Distillate fuel oil: A term subject to a variety of definitions. Sometimes the definition is based on the method of production, but other definitions are based on boiling range, viscosity, or use.

Distributor: A wholesaler of gasoline and other petroleum products; also known as a jobber. Distributors of natural gas are almost always regulated utility companies.

Domestic production: Oil and gas produced in the United States as opposed to imported product.

Downstream: All operations taking place after crude oil is produced, such as transportation, refining, and marketing.

Drainage basin: The land drained by a river system.

Drilling: The act of boring a hole to 1) determine whether minerals are present in commercially recoverable quantities and to 2) accomplish production of the minerals (including drilling to inject fluids).

- Exploratory: Drilling to locate probable mineral deposits or to establish the nature of geological structures; such wells may not be capable of production if minerals are discovered.

- Developmental: Drilling to delineate the boundaries of a known mineral deposit to enhance the productive capacity of the producing mineral property.
- Directional: Drilling that is deliberately made to depart significantly from the vertical.

Dry hole: An exploratory or development well found to be incapable of producing either oil or gas in sufficient quantities to justify completion as an oil or gas well.

Dry natural gas: Natural gas containing few or no natural gas liquids (liquid petroleum mixed with gas). Natural gas which remains after: 1) the liquefiable hydrocarbon portion has been removed from the gas stream (i.e., gas after lease, field, or plant separation); and 2) any volumes of non-hydrocarbon gases have been removed where they occur in sufficient quantity to render the gas unmarketable. **Note:** Dry natural gas is also known as consumer-grade natural gas. The parameters for measurement are cubic feet at 60°F and 14.73 pounds per square inch absolute.

Dual completion: Completing a well that draws from two or more separate producing formations at different depths. This is done by inserting multiple strings of tubing into the well casing and inserting packers to seal off all formations except the one to be produced by a particular string.

Dual-fuel vehicle (1): A motor vehicle that is capable of operating on an alternative fuel and on gasoline or diesel fuel. These vehicles have at least two separate fuel systems which inject each fuel simultaneously into the engine combustion chamber.

Dual-fuel vehicle (2): A motor vehicle that is capable of operating on an alternative fuel and on gasoline or diesel fuel. This term is meant to represent all such vehicles whether they operate on the alternative fuel and gasoline or diesel simultaneously (e.g., flexible-fuel vehicles) or can be switched to operate on gasoline or diesel or an alternative fuel (e.g., bifuel vehicles).

E

E85: A fuel containing a mixture of 85 percent ethanol and 15 percent gasoline.

E95: A fuel containing a mixture of 95 percent ethanol and 5 percent gasoline.

EAR: Estimated additional resources.

EIA: Energy Information Administration. An independent agency within the US Department of Energy that develops surveys, collects energy data, and analyzes and models energy issues. The Agency must meet the requests of Congress, other elements within the Department of Energy, Federal Energy Regulatory Commission, the Executive Branch, its own independent needs, and assist the general public or other interest groups, without taking a policy position.

EIS: Environmental impact statement.

Electric hybrid vehicle: An electric vehicle that either 1) operates solely on electricity but contains an internal combustion motor that generates additional electricity (series hybrid); or 2) contains an electric system and an internal combustion system and is capable of operating on either system (parallel hybrid).

Electric power grid: A system of synchronized power providers and consumers connected by transmission and distribution lines and operated by one or more control centers. In the continental United States, the electric power grid consists of three systems: the Eastern Interconnect, the Western Interconnect, and the Texas Interconnect. In Alaska and Hawaii, several systems encompass areas smaller than the state (e.g., the interconnect serving Anchorage, Fairbanks, and the Kenai Peninsula; individual islands).

Energy Policy Act of 1992 (EPACT): This legislation created a new class of power generators—exempt wholesale generators—that are exempt from the provisions of the Public Holding Company Act of 1935 and granted the authority to the Federal Energy Regulatory Commission to order and condition access by eligible parties to the interconnected transmission grid.

Enhanced oil recovery (EOR): Injection of water, steam, gases, or chemicals into underground reservoirs to cause oil to flow toward producing wells, permitting more than would have been possible from pumping natural pressure or pumping alone.

Enriched uranium: Uranium in which the U-235 isotope concentration has been increased to greater than the 0.711 percent U-235 (by weight) present in natural uranium.

Environmental impact statement: A report that documents the information required to evaluate the environmental impact of a project. It informs decision makers and the public of the reasonable alternatives that would avoid or minimize adverse impacts or enhance the quality of the environment.

EPA: Environmental Protection Agency.

ETBE: Ethyl tertiary butyl ether.

Ethane (C_2H_6): A normally gaseous straight-chain hydrocarbon. It is a colorless paraffinic gas that boils at a temperature of -127.48°F. It is extracted from natural gas and refinery gas streams.

Ethanol (C_2H_5OH): A clear, colorless, flammable alcohol. Ethanol is typically produced biologically from biomass feedstocks such as agricultural crops and cellulosic residues from agricultural crops or wood. Ethanol can also be produced chemically from ethylene. The two-carbon-atom alcohol present in the greatest proportion upon fermentation of grain and other renewable resources such as potatoes, sugar, or timber. Also called grain alcohol.

Exploration: The search for oil and gas. Exploration operations include: aerial surveys, geophysical surveys, geological studies, core testing, and the drilling of test wells.

Exploration drilling: Drilling done in search of new mineral deposits, on extensions of known ore deposits, or at the location of a discovery up to the time when the company decides that sufficient ore reserves are present to justify commercial exploration. Assessment drilling is reported as exploration drilling.

Exploratory well: A hole drilled to a) find and produce oil or gas in an area previously considered unproductive area; b) find a new reservoir in a known field, i.e., one previously producing oil and gas from another reservoir, or c) extend the limit of a known oil or gas reservoir.

Extraction plant: A plant for the extraction of the liquid constituents in casinghead gas or wet gas.

F

Farm out (in) arrangement: An arrangement, used primarily in the oil and gas industry, in which the owner or lessee of mineral rights (the first party) assigns a working interest to an operator (the second party), the consideration for which is specified exploration or development activities. The first party retains an overriding royalty or other type of economic interest in the mineral production. The arrangement from the viewpoint of the second party is termed a "farm-in arrangement."

Fault: A break in the continuity of strified rocks or even basement rocks. Faults are significant to oilmen because they can form traps for oil when the rock fractures; they can break oil reservoirs into non-communicating sections; they help produce oil accumulations; and they form traps on their own.

Fault trap: A geological formation in which oil or gas in a porous section of rock is sealed off by a displaced, nonporous layer.

Field: An area consisting of a single reservoir or multiple reservoirs all grouped on, or related to, the same individual geological structural feature or stratigraphic condition. There may be two or more reservoirs in a field that are separated vertically by intervening impervious strata or laterally by local geologic barriers, or by both.

Fischer-Tropsch: This method starts with partial oxidation of methane (natural gas) to carbon dioxide, carbon monoxide, hydrogen and water; the carbon monoxide to hydrogen (H_2) ratio is adjusted using the water gas shift reaction and the excess carbon dioxide removal by aqueous solutions of alkanolamine (or physical solvents); the water is removed yielding synthesis gas (syngas) that is chemically reacted over an iron or cobalt catalyst to produce liquid hydrocarbons and other byproducts.

Fission: The process whereby an atomic nucleus of appropriate type, after capturing a neutron, splits into (generally) two nuclei of lighter elements, with the release of substantial amounts of energy and two or more neutrons.

Flooding: One of the methods of enhanced oil recovery. Can be water or gas flooding.

Flowing well: A well that produces through natural reservoir pressure and does not require pumping.

Formation: A geological term that describes a succession of strata similar enough to form a distinctive geological unit useful for mapping or description.

Fossil fuel: An energy source formed in the Earth RSQUO's crust from decayed organic material. The common fossil fuels are petroleum, coal, and natural gas.

Fracturing: A well stimulation technique in which fluids are pumped into a formation under extremely high pressure to create or enlarge fractures for oil and gas to flow through. Proppants such as sand are injected with the liquid to hold the fractures open.

Fuel cell: A device capable of generating an electrical current by converting the chemical energy of a fuel (e.g., hydrogen) directly into electrical energy. Fuel cells differ from conventional electrical cells in that the active materials such as fuel and oxygen are not contained within the cell but are supplied from outside. It does not contain an intermediate heat cycle, as do most other electrical generation techniques.

Fuel oil: A liquid petroleum product less volatile than gasoline, used as an energy source. Fuel oil includes distillate fuel oil (No. 1, No. 2, and No. 4), and residual fuel oil (No. 5 and No. 6).

G

Gallon: A volumetric measure equal to 4 quarts (231 cubic inches) used to measure fuel oil. One barrel equals 42 gallons.

Gas cap: The gas that exists in a free state above the oil in a reservoir.

Gas condensate: Liquid hydrocarbons present in casinghead gas that condense when brought to the surface.

Gas lift: A recovery method that brings oil from the bottom of a well to the surface by using compressed gas. Gas pumped to the bottom of the reservoir mixes with fluid, expands it, and lifts it to the surface.

Gas to liquids (GTL): A process that combines the carbon and hydrogen elements in natural gas molecules to make synthetic liquid petroleum products, such as diesel fuel.

Gas–oil ratio: The number of cubic feet of natural gas produced along with a barrel of oil.

Gas well: A well completed for production of natural gas from one or more gas zones or reservoirs. Such wells contain no completions for the production of crude oil.

Gasoline: A volatile, inflammable, liquid hydrocarbon mixture.

Gasoline blending components: Naphthas which will be used for blending or compounding into finished aviation or motor gasoline (e.g., straight-run gasoline, alkylate, reformate, benzene, toluene, andxylene). Excludes oxygenates (alcohols, ethers), butane, and pentanes plus.

Gasoline grades: The classification of gasoline by octane ratings. Each type of gasoline (conventional, oxygenated, and reformulated) is classified by three grades—regular, midgrade, and premium. **Note:** Gasoline sales are reported by grade in accordance with their classification at the time of sale. In general, automotive octane requirements are lower at high altitudes. Therefore, in some areas of the United States, such as the Rocky Mountain States, the octane ratings for the gasoline grades may be two or more octane points lower.

> **Regular gasoline:** Gasoline having an antiknock index, i.e., octane rating, greater than or equal to 85 and less than 88. **Note:** Octane requirements may vary by altitude.

> **Midgrade gasoline:** Gasoline having an antiknock index, i.e., octane rating, greater than or equal to 88 and less than or equal to 90. **Note:** Octane requirements may vary by altitude.

> **Premium gasoline:** Gasoline having an antiknock index, i.e., octane rating, greater than 90. **Note:** Octane requirements may vary by altitudes or fluids at various depths beneath the surface of the earth. The energy is extracted by drilling or pumping.

Geophones: The sound-detecting instruments used to measure sound waves created by expolosions set off during seismic exploration work.

Geophysicist: A geophysicist applies the principles of physics to the understanding of geology.

Geopressured: A type of geothermal resource occurring in deep basins in which the fluid is under very high pressure.

Geothermal energy: Hot water or steam extracted from geothermal reservoirs in the earth's crust. Water or steam extracted from geothermal reservoirs can be used for geothermal heat pumps, water heating, or electricity generation.

Gigawatt (GW): One billion watts or one thousand megawatts.

Gigawatt-electric (GWe): One billion watts of electric capacity.

Gigawatthour (GWh): One billion watt-hours.

Greenhouse gases: Those gases, such as water vapor, carbon dioxide, nitrous oxide, methane, hydrofluorocarbons (HFCs), perfluorocarbons (PFCs) and sulfur hexafluoride, that are transparent to solar (short-wave) radiation but opaque to long-wave (infrared) radiation, thus preventing long-wave radiant energy from leaving earth's atmosphere. The net effect is a trapping of absorbed radiation and a tendency to warm the planet's surface.

Grid: The layout of an electrical distribution system.

Gun perforation: A method of creating holes in a well casing downhole by exploding charges to propel steel projectiles through the casing wall. Such holes allow oil from the formation to enter the well.

Gusher: A well drilled into a formation in which the crude is under such high pressure that at first it spurts out of the wellhead like a geyser. Gushers are rare today owing to improved drilling technology, the use of drilling mud to control downhole pressure, and oilmen's recognition of their wastefulness.

H

Heating oil: Oil used for residential heating.

Heat(ing) pump: A heat pump is a machine or device that transfers thermal energy from one location called the "source," which is at a lower temperature, to another location called the "sink" or "heat sink," which is at a higher temperature. While compressor-driven air conditioners and freezers are technically heat pumps, the class includes many other types of devices, and the term "heat pump" usually implies one of the less-common devices in the class that are not dedicated to refrigeration-only.

Heavy oil: A type of crude petroleum characterized by viscosity and a high carbon-to-hydrogen ratio. It is usually difficult and costly to produce by conventional techniques.

Hedging: The buying and selling of futures contracts so as to protect energy traders from unexpected or adverse price fluctuations.

Hedging contracts: Contracts that establish future prices and quantities of electricity independent of the short-term market. Derivatives may be used for this purpose.

Henry Hub: A pipeline hub on the Louisiana Gulf Coast. It is the delivery point for the natural gas futures contract on the New York Mercantile Exchange (NYMEX).

Hydraulic fracturing: Fracturing of rock at depth with fluid pressure. Hydraulic fracturing at depth may be accomplished by pumping water into a well at very high pressures. Under natural conditions, vapor pressure may rise high enough to cause fracturing in a process known as hydrothermal brecciation.

Hydrocarbon: An organic chemical compound of hydrogen and carbon in the gaseous, liquid, or solid phase. The molecular structure of hydrocarbon compounds varies from the simplest (methane, a constituent of natural gas) to the very heavy and complex.

Hydrochlorofluorocarbons (HCFCs): Chemicals composed of one or more carbon atoms and varying numbers of hydrogen, chlorine, and fluorine atoms.

Hydroelectric power: The use of flowing water to produce electrical energy.

Hydrofluorocarbons (HFCs): A group of man-made chemicals composed of one or two carbon atoms and varying numbers of hydrogen and fluorine atoms. Most HFCs have one-hundred-year global warming potentials in the thousands.

Hydrogen: The lightest of all gases, occurring chiefly in combination with oxygen in water; exists also in acids, bases, alcohols, petroleum, and other hydrocarbons.

I

Independent producer: 1) A person or corporation that produces oil for the market, who has no pipeline system or refining capability. 2) An oil entrepreneur who secures financial backing and drills his own wells.

Injections: Natural gas injected into storage reservoirs.

Intangible drilling and development costs (IDC): Costs incurred in preparing well locations, drilling and deepening wells, and preparing wells for initial production up through the point of installing control valves. None of these functions, because of their nature, have salvage value. Such costs would include labor, transportation, consumable supplies, drilling tool rentals, site clearance, and similar costs.

Internal combustion plant: A plant in which the prime mover is an internal combustion engine. An internal combustion engine has one or more cylinders in which the process of combustion takes place, converting energy released from the rapid burning of a fuel-air mixture into mechanical energy. Diesel or gas-fired engines are the principal types used in electric plants. The plant is usually operated during periods of high demand for electricity.

J

Jack-up rig: A floating platform with legs on each corner that can be lowered to the sea bottom to raise or jack the platform above the water.

Jet fuel: A refined petroleum product used in jet aircraft engines. It includes kerosene-type jet fuel and naphtha-type jet fuel.

Joint operating agreement: A detailed written agreement between the working interest owners of a property that specifies the terms according to which that property will be developed.

Joint venture: A large-scale project in which two or more parties (usually oil companies) cooperate. One supplies funds and the other actually carries out the work.

K

Kerogen: The hydrocarbon in oil shale. Scientists believe that kerogen was the precursor of petroleum development in shale that was somehow prematurely arrested.

Kerosene: A light petroleum distillate that is used in space heaters, cook stoves, and water heaters and is suitable for use as a light source when burned in wick-fed lamps. Kerosene has a maximum distillation temperature of 400°F at the 10 percent recovery point, a final boiling point of 572°F, and a minimum flash point of 100°F. Included are No. 1-K and No. 2-K, the two grades recognized by ASTM Specification D3699, as well as all other grades of kerosene called range or stove oil, which have properties similar to those of No. 1 fuel oil.

Kilowatt (kW): One thousand watts.

Kilowatt-electric (kWe): One thousand watts of electric capacity.

Kilowatthour (kWh): A measure of electricity defined as a unit of work or energy, measured as 1 kilowatt (1,000 watts) of power expended for 1 hour. One kWh is equivalent to 3,412 Btu.

Kinetic energy: Energy available as a result of motion that varies directly in proportion to an object's mass and the square of its velocity.

L

Lifting costs: The costs associated with the extraction of a mineral reserve from a producing property.

Light gas oils: Liquid petroleum distillates heavier than naphtha, with an approximate boiling range from 401°F to 650°F.

Light trucks: All single unit, two-axle, four-tire trucks, including pickup trucks, sports utility vehicles, vans, motor homes, etc. This is the Department of Transportation definition. The Energy Information Administration defines light truck as all trucks weighing 8,500 pounds or less.

Lignite: The lowest rank of coal, often referred to as brown coal, used almost exclusively as fuel for steam-electric power generation. It is brownish-black and has a high inherent moisture content, sometimes as high as 45 percent. The heat content of lignite ranges from 9 to 17 million Btu per ton on a moist, mineral-matter-free basis. The heat content of lignite consumed in the United States averages 13 million Btu per ton, on the as-received basis (i.e., containing both inherent moisture and mineral matter).

Limestone: Sedimentary rock largely consisting of calcite. On a world-wide scale, limestone reservoirs probably contain more oil and gas reserves than all other types of reservoir rock combined.

Lithium: A soft, silver-white metal that belongs to the alkali metal group of chemical elements. It is represented by the symbol Li, and it has the atomic number 3. A lithium-ion battery (sometimes li-ion battery or LIB) is a family of rechargeable battery types in which lithium ions move from the negative electrode to the positive electrode during discharge, and back when charging. Chemistry, performance, cost, and safety characteristics vary across LIB types. Unlike lithium primary batteries (which are disposable), lithium-ion electrochemical cells use an intercalated lithium compound as the electrode material instead of metallic lithium.

Liquefied natural gas (LNG): Natural gas (primarily methane) that has been liquefied by reducing its temperature to -260°F at atmospheric pressure.

Liquefied petroleum gases (LPG): A group of hydrocarbon-based gases derived from crude oil refining or natural gas fractionation. They include ethane, ethylene, propane, propylene, normal butane, butylene, isobutane, and isobutylene. For convenience of transportation, these gases are liquefied through pressurization.

Load (electric): An end-use device or customer that receives power from the electric system.

Lubricants: Substances used to reduce friction between bearing surfaces, or incorporated into other materials as processing aids in the manufacture of other products, or used as carriers of other materials. Petroleum lubricants may be produced either from distillates or residues. Lubricants include all grades of lubricating oils, from spindle oil to cylinder oil to those used in greases.

Lumen: An empirical measure of the quantity of light. It is based upon the spectral sensitivity of the photosensors in the human eye under high (daytime) light levels. Photometrically it is the luminous flux emitted with a solid angle (1 steradian) by a point source having a uniform luminous intensity of 1 candela.

M

M: Thousand.

MBOED: Million barrels of oil equivalent per day.

Mcf: One thousand cubic feet.

Megawatt (MW): One million watts of electricity.

Megawatt electric (MWe): One million watts of electric capacity.

Megawatthour (MWh): One thousand kilowatt-hours or 1 million watt-hours.

Methane: A colorless, flammable, odorless hydrocarbon gas (CH_4) that is the major component of natural gas. It is also an important source of hydrogen in various industrial processes. Methane is a greenhouse gas.

Methanogens: Bacteria that synthesize methane, requiring completely anaerobic conditions for growth.

Methanol (CH_3OH): A light, volatile alcohol eligible for gasoline blending.

Methanol blend: Mixtures containing 85 percent or more (or such other percentage, but not less than 70 percent) by volume of methanol with gasoline. Pure methanol is considered an "other alternative fuel."

Mid-continent crude: Oil produced mainly in Kansas, Oklahoma, and North Texas.

Midstream or middle distillates: Refinery products in the middle of the distillation range of crude oil, including kerosene-based jet fuel, home heating fuel, range oil, stove oil, and diesel fuel.

MM: Million.

MMbbl/d: One million barrels of oil per day.

MMBtu: One million British thermal units.

MMcf: One million cubic feet.

MMgal/d: One million gallons per day.

MMst: One million short tons.

MTBE (methyl tertiary butyl ether) $(CH_3)_3COCH_3$: An ether intended for gasoline blending as described in **Oxygenates.**

Mud: A fluid mixture of clay, chemicals, and weighting materials suspended in fresh water, salt water, or diesel oil.

MW: Megawatt.

MWe: Megawatt electricity.

MWh: Megawatt hour.

N

N_2O: Nitrous oxide.

NAAQS: National ambient air quality standards.

NAICS (North American Industry Classification System): A coding system developed jointly by the United States, Canada, and Mexico to classify businesses and industries according to the type of economic activity in which they are engaged. NAICS replaces the Standard Industrial Classification (SIC) codes.

Naphtha: A generic term applied to a petroleum fraction with an approximate boiling range between 122°F and 400°F.

Naphthas: Refined or partly refined light distillates with an approximate boiling point range of 27°C to 221°C. Blended further or mixed with other materials, they make high-grade motor gasoline or jet fuel. Also used as solvents, petrochemical feedstocks, or as raw materials for the production of town gas.

National Association of Regulatory Utility Commissioners (NARUC): An affiliation of the public service commissioners to promote the uniform treatment of members of the railroad, public utilities, and public service commissions of the fifty states, the District of Columbia, the Commonwealth of Puerto Rico, and the territory of the Virgin Islands.

Natural gas: A gaseous mixture of hydrocarbon compounds, the primary one being methane.

Natural gas processing plant: Facilities designed to recover natural gas liquids from a stream of natural gas that may or may not have passed through lease separators or field separation facilities. These facilities control the quality of the natural gas to be marketed. Cycling plants are classified as gas processing plants.

Naval petroleum reserves: Areas containing proven oil reserves that were set aside for national defense purposes by Congress in 1923 (located in Elk Hills and Buena Vista, California; Teapot Dome, Wyoming; and on the North Slope in Alaska).

Net energy for load (electric): Net balancing authority area generation, plus energy received from other balancing authority areas, less energy delivered to balancing authority areas through interchange. It includes balancing authority area losses but excludes energy required for storage at energy storage facilities (NERC definition).

Net energy for system: The sum of energy an electric utility needs to satisfy their service areas, including full and partial requirements consumers.

Net generation: The amount of gross generation less the electrical energy consumed at the generating station(s) for station service or auxiliaries. **Note:** Electricity required for pumping at pumped-storage plants is regarded as electricity for station service and is deducted from gross generation.

Net head: The gross head minus all hydraulic losses except those chargeable to the turbine.

Net interstate flow of electricity: The difference between the sum of electricity sales and losses within a state and the total amount of electricity generated within that state. A positive number indicates that more electricity (including associated losses) came into the state than went out of the state during the year; conversely, a negative number indicates that more electricity (including associated losses) went out of the state than came into the state.

Net summer capacity: The maximum output, commonly expressed in megawatts (MW), that generating equipment can supply to system load, as demonstrated by a multi-hour test, at the time of summer peak demand (period of June 1 through September 30.) This output reflects a reduction in capacity due to electricity use for station service or auxiliaries.

Net winter capacity: The maximum output, commonly expressed in megawatts (MW), that generating equipment can supply to system load, as demonstrated by a multi-hour test, at the time of peak winter demand (period of December 1 through February 28). This output reflects a reduction in capacity due to electricity use for station service or auxiliaries.

Netback purchase: Refers to a crude oil purchase agreement wherein the price paid for the crude is determined by sales prices of the types of products that are derivable from that crude as well as other considerations (e.g., transportation and processing costs). Typically, the price is calculated based on product prices extant on or near the cargo's date of importation.

NGL: Portions of natural gas that are liquefied at the surface in lease separators, field facilities, or gas processing plants, leaving dry natural. They include, but are not limited to, ethane, propane, butane, natural gasoline, and condensate.

NGPA: Natural Gas Policy Act of 1978.

NGV: Natural gas vehicle.

Nitrogen dioxide: A compound of nitrogen and oxygen formed by the oxidation of nitric oxide (NO), which is produced by the combustion of solid fuels.

Nitrogen oxides (NOx): Compounds of nitrogen and oxygen produced by the burning of fossil fuels.

Nitrous oxide (N_2O): A colorless gas, naturally occurring in the atmosphere. Nitrous oxide has a one-hundred-year global warming potential of 310.

Nonattainment area: Any area that does not meet the national primary or secondary ambient air quality standard established by the Environmental Protection Agency for designated pollutants, such as carbon monoxide and ozone.

Nuclear fuel: Fissionable materials that have been enriched to such a composition that, when placed in a nuclear reactor, will support a self-sustaining fission chain reaction, producing heat in a controlled manner for process use.

Nuclear reactor: An apparatus in which a nuclear fission chain reaction can be initiated, controlled, and sustained at a specific rate. A reactor includes fuel (fissionable material), moderating material to control the rate of fission, a heavy-walled pressure vessel to house reactor components, shielding to protect personnel, a system to conduct heat away from the reactor, and instrumentation for monitoring and controlling the reactor's systems.

O

Octane: A flammable liquid hydrocarbon found in petroleum. Used as a standard to measure the antiknock properties of motor fuel.

Octane rating: A number used to indicate gasoline's antiknock performance in motor vehicle engines. The two recognized laboratory engine test methods for determining the antiknock rating, i.e., octane rating of gasoline, are the research method and the motor method. To provide a single number as guidance to the consumer, the antiknock index $(R + M) / 2$, which is the average of the research and motor octane numbers, was developed.

OECD (Organization for Economic Cooperation and Development): An international organization helping governments tackle the economic, socia, and governance challenges of a globalized economy. Its membership comprises about thirty member countries. With active relationships with some seventy other countries, non-governmental organizations (NGOs), and civil society, it has a global reach. For details about the organization, visit www.OECD.org.

OEM: An original equipment manufacturer manufactures products or components that are purchased by a company and retailed under that purchasing company's brand name.

Off peak: Period of relatively low system demand. These periods often occur in daily, weekly, and seasonal patterns; these off-peak periods differ for each individual electric utility.

Oil shale: A sedimentary rock containing kerogen, a solid organic material.

Oil stocks: Oil stocks include crude oil (including strategic reserves), unfinished oils, natural gas plant liquids, and refined petroleum products.

Oil well: A well completed for the production of crude oil from at least one oil zone or reservoir.

OPEC (Organization of the Petroleum Exporting Countries): An intergovernmental organization whose stated objective is to "coordinate and unify the petroleum policies of member countries." It was created at the Baghdad Conference on September 10–14, 1960. Current members include:

- Algeria (1969–present)
- Angola (2007–present)
- Ecuador (1973–1992 and 2007–present)
- Iran (1960–present)
- Iraq (1960–present)
- Kuwait (1960–present)
- Libya (1962–present)
- Nigeria (1971–present)
- Qatar (1961–present)
- Saudi Arabia (1960–present)
- United Arab Emirates (1967–present)
- Venezuela (1960–present)

Countries no longer members of OPEC include:
- Gabon (1975–1994)
- Indonesia (1962–2008)

Operator, oil or gas well: The person responsible for the management and day-to-day operation of one or more crude oil or natural gas wells as of December 31 of the report year. The operator is generally a working-interest owner or a company under contract to the working-interest owner(s). Wells included are those that have proved reserves of crude oil, natural gas, or lease condensate in the reservoirs associated with them, whether or not they are producing. Wells abandoned during the report year are also to be considered "operated" as of December 31.

Overriding royalty: A royalty interest, in addition to the basic royalty, created out of the working interest; it is, therefore, limited in its duration to the life of the lease under which it is created.

Oxygenates: Substances which, when added to gasoline, increase the amount of oxygen in that gasoline blend.

P

Paraffin (wax): The wax removed from paraffin distillates by chilling and pressing. When separating from solutions, it is a colorless, more or less translucent, crystalline mass, without odor or taste, slightly greasy to touch, and consisting of a mixture of solid hydrocarbons in which the paraffin series predominates.

Peak demand: The maximum demand during a specified period of time.

Peak kilowatt: One thousand peak watts.

Peak load: The maximum load during a specified period of time.

Perforating gun: An instrument lowered at the end of wireline into a cased well. It contains explosive charges that can be electronically detonated from the surface.

Perforation: A method of making holes through the casing opposite the producing formation to allow the oil and gas to flow into the well.

Perfluorocarbons (PFCs): A group of man-made chemicals composed of one or two carbon atoms and four to six fluorine atoms, containing no chlorine. PFCs have no commercial uses and are emitted as a byproduct of aluminum smelting and semiconductor manufacturing. PFCs have very high one-hundred-year global warming potentials and are very long-lived in the atmosphere.

Perfluoromethane: A compound (CF_4) emitted as a byproduct of aluminum smelting.

Permanently discharged fuel: Spent nuclear fuel for which there are no plans for reinsertion in the reactor core.

Permeability: The ease with which fluid flows through a porous medium.

Petrochemicals: Organic and inorganic compounds and mixtures that include but are not limited to organic chemicals, cyclic intermediates, plastics and resins, synthetic fibers, elastomers, organic dyes, organic pigments, detergents, surface active agents, carbon black, and ammonia.

Petroleum: A broadly defined class of liquid hydrocarbon mixtures. Included is crude oil, lease condensate, unfinished oils, refined products obtained from the processing of crude oil, and natural gas plant liquids. **Note:** Volumes of finished petroleum products include non-hydrocarbon compounds, such as additives and detergents, after they have been blended into the products.

Petroleum products: Petroleum products are obtained from the processing of crude oil (including lease condensate), natural gas, and other hydrocarbon compounds. Petroleum products include unfinished oils, liquefied petroleum gases, pentanes plus, aviation gasoline, motor gasoline, naphtha-type jet fuel, kerosene-type jet fuel, kerosene, distillate fuel oil, residual fuel oil, petrochemical feedstocks, special naphthas, lubricants, waxes, petroleum coke, asphalt, road oil, still gas, and miscellaneous products.

Petroleum refinery: An installation that manufactures finished petroleum products from crude oil, unfinished oils, natural gas liquids, other hydrocarbons, and alcohol.

Photovoltaic cell (PVC): An electronic device consisting of layers of semiconductor materials fabricated to form a junction (adjacent layers of materials with different electronic characteristics) and electrical contacts and being capable of converting incident light directly into electricity (direct current).

Photovoltaic cell net shipments: Represents the difference between photovoltaic cell shipments and photovoltaic cell purchases.

Photovoltaic module: An integrated assembly of interconnected photovoltaic cells designed to deliver a selected level of working voltage and current at its output terminals, packaged for protection against environmental degradation, and suited for incorporation in photovoltaic power systems.

Pipeline (natural gas): A continuous pipe conduit, complete with such equipment as valves, compressor stations, communications systems, and meters for transporting natural or supplemental gas from one point to another, usually from a point in or beyond the producing field or processing plant to another pipeline or to points of utilization. Also refers to a company operating such facilities.

Pipeline (petroleum): Crude oil and product pipelines used to transport crude oil and petroleum products, respectively (including interstate, intrastate, and intracompany pipelines), within the fifty states and the District of Columbia.

Plant condensate: One of the natural gas liquids, mostly pentanes and heavier hydrocarbons, recovered and separated as liquids at gas inlet separators or scrubbers in processing plants.

Plant liquids: Those volumes of natural gas liquids recovered in natural gas processing plants.

Plant or gas processing plant: A facility designated to achieve the recovery of natural gas liquids from the stream of natural gas, which may or may not have been processed through lease separators and field facilities, and to control the quality of the natural gas to be marketed.

Plugging a well: Filling the borehole of an abandoned well with mud and cement to prevent the flow of water or oil from one strata to another or to the surface.

Porosity: A measure of the number and size of the spaces between each particle in a rock. Porosity affects the amount of liquid and gases, such as natural gas and crude oil, that a given reservoir can contain.

Possible reserves: Areas in which production of crude oil is presumed possible owing to geological inference of a strongly speculative nature.

Primary recovery: The crude oil or natural gas recovered by any method that may be employed to produce them where the fluid enters the well bore by the action of natural reservoir pressure (energy or gravity).

Probable energy reserves: Estimated quantities of energy sources that, on the basis of geologic evidence that supports projections from proved reserves, can reasonably be expected to exist and be recoverable under existing economic and operating conditions. Site information is insufficient to establish with confidence the location, quality, and grades of the energy source. **Note:** This term is equivalent to "indicated reserves" as defined in the resource–reserve classification contained in the US Geological Survey Circular 831, 1980. Measured and indicated reserves, when combined, constitute demonstrated reserves.

Producer: A company engaged in the production and sale of natural gas from gas or oil wells with delivery generally at a point at or near the wellhead, the field, or the tailgate of a gas processing plant. For the purpose of company classification, a company primarily engaged in the exploration for, development of, or production of oil or natural gas.

Production: A term commonly used to describe taking natural ground.

Proved energy reserves: Estimated quantities of energy sources that analysis of geologic and engineering data demonstrates with reasonable certainty are recoverable under existing economic and operating conditions. The location, quantity, and grade of the energy source are usually considered to be well established in such reserves. **Note:** This term is equivalent to "measured reserves" as defined in the resource–reserve classification contained in the US Geological Survey Circular 831, 1980. Measured and indicated reserves, when combined, constitute demonstrated reserves.

PUHCA: The Public Utility Holding Company Act of 1935 (PUHCA), also known as the Wheeler-Rayburn Act, was a law passed by the United States Congress to facilitate regulation of electric utilities, by either limiting their operations to a single state and thus subjecting them to effective state regulation, or forcing divestitures so that each became a single integrated system serving a limited geographic area.

PURPA (Public Utility Regulatory Policies Act): A law passed in 1978 by the United States Congress as part of the National Energy Act. It is meant to promote greater use of domestic renewable energy. The law forced regulated, natural monopoly electric utilities to buy power from other more efficient producers, if that cost was less than the utility's own "avoided cost" rate to the consumer; the avoided cost rate was the additional costs that the electric utility would incur if it generated the required power itself, or if available, could purchase its demand requirements from another source.

PV: Photovoltaic.

PVC (PVCs that convert sunlight directly into energy): A method for producing energy by converting sunlight using photovoltaic cells (PVCs) that are solid-state single converter devices. Although not currently in wide usage, commercial customers have a growing interest in usage and therefore, DOE has a growing interest in the impact of PVCs on energy consumption. Economically, PVCs are competitive with other sources of electricity.

Q

QUAD: Quadrillion Btu 1015 Btu.

Quadrillion: The quantity 1,000,000,000,000,000 (10 to the 15th power).

R

R-value: A measure of a material's resistance to heat flow in units of F degrees × hours × square feet per Btu. The higher the R-value of a material, the greater its insulating capability. The R-value of some insulating materials is 3.7 per inch for fiber glass and cellulose, 2.5 per inch for vermiculite, and more than 4 per inch for foam. All building materials have some R-value.

Radon: A naturally occurring radioactive gas found in the United States in nearly all types of soil, rock, and water. It can migrate into most buildings. Studies have linked high concentrations of radon to lung cancer.

Recoverable resources: An estimate of resources, including oil and natural gas, both proved and undiscovered, that would be economically extractable under specified price-cost relationships and technological conditions.

Reclamation: Process of restoring surface environment to acceptable preexisting conditions. Includes surface contouring, equipment removal, well plugging, revegetation, etc.

Refining: Manufacturing petroleum products by a series of processes that separate crude oil into its major components and blend or convert these components into a wide range of finished products, such as gasoline or jet fuel.

Refinery: An installation that manufactures finished petroleum products from crude oil, unfinished oils, natural gas liquids, other hydrocarbons, and oxygenates.

Reformulated gasoline: Finished gasoline formulated for use in motor vehicles, the composition and properties of which meet the requirements of the reformulated gasoline regulations promulgated by the US Environmental Protection Agency under Section 211(k) of the Clean Air Act. It includes gasoline produced to meet or exceed emissions performance and benzene content standards of federal-program reformulated gasoline even though the gasoline may not meet all of the composition requirements (e.g., oxygen content) of federal-program reformulated gasoline. **Note:** This category includes Oxygenated Fuels Program Reformulated Gasoline (OPRG). Reformulated gasoline excludes Reformulated Blendstock for Oxygenate Blending (RBOB) and Gasoline Treated as Blendstock (GTAB).

Reserve: That portion of the demonstrated reserve base that is estimated to be recoverable at the time of determination. The reserve is derived by applying a recovery factor to that component of the identified coal resource designated as the demonstrated reserve base.

Reservoir: A porous and permeable underground formation containing an individual and separate natural accumulation of producible hydrocarbons (crude oil and natural gas) that is confined by impermeable rock or water barriers and is characterized by a single natural pressure system.

Residual fuel oil: A general classification for the heavier oils, known as No. 5 and No. 6 fuel oils, that remain after the distillate fuel oils and lighter hydrocarbons are distilled away in refinery operations. It conforms to ASTM Specifications D396 and D975 and Federal Specification VV-F-815C. No. 5, a residual fuel oil of medium viscosity, is also known as Navy Special and is defined in Military Specification MIL-F-859E, including Amendment 2 (NATO SymbolF-770). It is used in steam-powered vessels in government service and inshore power plants. No. 6 fuel oil includes Bunker C fuel oil and is issued for the production of electric power, space heating, vessel bunkering, and various industrial purposes.

Residue gas: Natural gas from which natural gas processing plant liquid products and, in some cases, non-hydrocarbon components have been extracted.

Rotary rig: A machine used for drilling wells that employs a rotating tube attached to a bit for boring holes through rock.

Royalty: A contractual arrangement providing a mineral interest that gives the owner a right to a fractional share of production or proceeds there from, that does not contain rights and obligations of operating a mineral property, and that is normally free and clear of exploration and developmental and operating costs, except production taxes.

Rural Electrification Administration (REA): A lending agency of the US Department of Agriculture, the REA makes self-liquidating loans to qualified borrowers to finance electric and telephone service to rural areas. The REA finances the construction and operation of generating plants, electric transmission and distribution lines, or systems for the furnishing of initial and continued adequate electric services to persons in rural areas not receiving central station service.

S

Salt dome: A domical arch (anticline) of sedimentary rock beneath the earth's surface in which the layers bend downward in opposite directions from the crest and that has a mass of rock salt as its core.

Salt gradient solar ponds: These consist of three main layers. The top layer is near ambient and has low salt content. The bottom layer is hot, typically 160°F to 212°F (71°C to 100°C), and is very salty. The important gradient zone separates these zones. The gradient zone acts as a transparent insulator, permitting the sunlight to be trapped in the hot bottom layer (from which useful heat is withdrawn). This is because the salt gradient, which increases the brine density with depth, counteracts the buoyancy effect of the warmer water below (which would otherwise rise to the surface and lose its heat to the air). An organic Rankine cycle engine is used to convert the thermal energy to electricity.

Secondary recovery: The introduction of water or gas into a well to supplement the natural reservoir drive and force additional oil to the producing wells.

Sedimentary basin: A large land area composed of unmetamorphized sediments. Oil and gas commonly occur in such formations.

Sedimentary rock: Rock formed by the deposition of sediment, usually in a marine environment.

Seismic exploration: A method of prospecting for oil or gas by sending shock waves at different speeds, so when vibrations at the surface send sound waves into the earth in all directions, they reflect to the surface at a distance and angle from the sound source that indicates the depth of the interface. These reflections are recorded and analyzed to map underground formations.

Service well: A well drilled, completed, or converted for the purpose of supporting production in an existing field. Wells of this class also are drilled or converted for the following specific purposes: gas injection (natural gas, propane, butane, or fuel-gas); water injection; steam injection; air injection; salt water disposal; water supply for injection; observation; and injection for in-situ combustion.

Shale: A fine-grained, clastic sedimentary rock composed of mud that is a mix of flakes of clay minerals and tiny fragments (silt-sized particles) of other minerals, especially quartz and calcite.

Shale gas: Natural gas produced from organic (black) shale formations.

Shrinkage: The volume of natural gas that is transformed into liquid products during processing, primarily at natural gas liquids processing plants.

Shut in: Closed temporarily; wells and mines capable of production may be shut in for repair, cleaning, inaccessibility to a market, etc.

Shut-in royalty: A royalty paid by a lessee as compensation for a lessor's loss of income because the lessee has deferred production from a property that is known to be capable of producing minerals. Shut in may be caused by a lack of a ready market, by a lack of transportation facilities, or by other reasons. A shut-in royalty may or may not be recoverable out of future production.

Sidetrack drilling: This is a remedial operation that results in the creation of a new section of well bored for the purpose of 1) detouring around junk, 2) redrilling lost holes, or 3) straightening key seats and crooked holes. Directional "side-track" wells do not include footage in the common bore that is reported as footage for the original well.

Sludge: A dense, slushy, liquid-to-semifluid product that accumulates as an end result of an industrial or technological process designed to purify a substance. Industrial sludges are produced from the processing of energy-related raw materials, chemical products, water, mined ores, sewerage, and other natural and man-made products. Sludges can also form from natural processes, such as the run off produced by rainfall, and accumulate on the bottom of bogs, streams, lakes, and tidelands.

Slurry: A viscous liquid with a high solids content.

Solar cell: A solid state electrical device that converts the energy of light directly into electricity by the photovoltaic effect. Also called photovoltaic cell or photoelectric cell.

Solar energy: The radiant energy of the sun, which can be converted into other forms of energy, such as heat or electricity.

Solar pond: A body of water that contains brackish (highly saline) water that forms layers of differing salinity (stratifies) that absorb and trap solar energy. Solar ponds can be used to provide heat for industrial or agricultural processes, building heating and cooling, and to generate electricity.

Solar power tower: A solar energy conversion system that uses a large field of independently adjustable mirrors (heliostats) to focus solar rays on a near single point atop a fixed tower (receiver). The concentrated energy may be used to directly heat the working fluid of a Rankine cycle engine or to heat an intermediary thermal storage medium (such as a molten salt).

Solar radiation: A general term for the visible and near visible (ultraviolet and near-infrared) electromagnetic radiation that is emitted by the sun. It has a spectral, or wavelength, distribution that corresponds to different energy levels; short wavelength radiation has a higher energy than long-wavelength radiation.

Spent fuel: Irradiated fuel that is permanently discharged from a reactor. Except for possible reprocessing, this fuel must eventually be removed from its temporary storage location at the reactor site and placed in a permanent repository. Spent fuel is typically measured either in metric tons of heavy metal (i.e., only the heavy metal content of the spent fuel is considered) or in metric tons of initial heavy metal (essentially, the initial mass of the fuel before irradiation). The difference between these two quantities is the weight of the fission products.

Spot market (natural gas): A market in which natural gas is bought and sold for immediate or very near-term delivery, usually for a period of thirty days or less. The transaction does not imply a continuing arrangement between the buyer and the seller. A spot market is more likely to develop at a location with numerous pipeline interconnections, thus allowing for a large number of buyers and sellers. The Henry Hub in southern Louisiana is the best known spot market for natural gas.

Spot price: The price for a one-time open market transaction for near-term delivery of a specific quantity of product at a specific location where the commodity is purchased at current market rates. See also spot market terms associated with specific energy types.

State severance taxes: Any severance, production, or similar tax, fee, or other levy imposed on the production of crude oil, natural gas, or coal by any state or local government acting under authority of state law, or by an Indian tribe recognized as eligible for services by the Department of the Interior.

Stranded costs: Costs incurred by a utility which may not be recoverable under market-based retail competition. Examples include undepreciated generating facilities, deferred costs, and long-term contract costs.

Stranded natural gas: A stranded gas reserve is found in a natural gas field that has been discovered but remains unusable for either physical or economic reasons. Gas that is found within an oil well is conventionally regarded as associated gas and has historically been flared.

Strategic petroleum reserve (SPR): Petroleum stocks maintained by the federal government for use during periods of major supply interruption.

Stratigraphic test well: A geologically directed drilling effort to obtain information pertaining to a specific geological condition that might lead toward the discovery of an accumulation of hydrocarbons. Such wells are customarily drilled without the intention of being completed for hydrocarbon production. This classification also includes tests identified as core tests and all types of expendable holes related to hydrocarbon exploration.

Strip mine: An open cut in which the over burden is removed from a coal bed prior to the removal of coal.

Strip mining (surface): A method used on flat terrain to recover coal by mining long strips successively; the material excavated from the strip being mined is deposited in the strip previously mined.

Stripper well: An oil or gas well that produces at relatively low rates. For oil, stripper production is usually defined as production rates of between five and fifteen barrels of oil per day. Stripper gas production would generally be anything less than sixty thousand cubic feet per day.

Sulfur: A yellowish nonmetallic element, sometimes known as "brimstone." It is present at various levels of concentration in many fossil fuels whose combustion releases sulfur compounds that are considered harmful to the environment. Some of the most commonly used fossil fuels are categorized according to their sulfur content, with lower sulfur fuels usually selling at a higher price. **Note:** No. 2 Distillate fuel is currently reported as having either a 0.05 percent or lower sulfur level for on-highway vehicle use or a greater than 0.05 percent sulfur level for off-highway use, home heating oil, and commercial and industrial uses. Residual fuel, regardless of use, is classified as having either no more than 1 percent sulfur or greater than 1 percent sulfur. Coal is also classified as being low-sulfur at concentrations of 1 percent or less or high-sulfur at concentrations greater than 1 percent.

Sulfur dioxide (SO_2): A toxic, irritating, colorless gas soluble in water, alcohol, and ether. Used as a chemical intermediate, in paper pulping and ore refining, and as a solvent.

Sulfur oxides (SOx): Compounds containing sulfur and oxygen, such as sulfur dioxide (SO_2) and sulfur trioxide (SO_3).

Summer and winter peaking: Having the annual peak demand reached both during the summer months (May through October) and during the winter months (November through April).

Supplemental gas: Any gaseous substance introduced into or commingled with natural gas that increased the volume available for disposition. Such substances include, but are not limited to, propane-air, refinery gas, coke-oven gas, still gas, manufactured gas, biomass gas, or air or inerts added for Btu stabilization.

Supplemental gaseous fuels supplies: Synthetic natural gas, propane-air, coke oven gas, refinery gas, biomass gas, air injected for Btu stabilization, and manufactured gas commingled and distributed with natural gas.

Supply: The components of petroleum supply are field production, refinery production, imports, and net receipts when calculated on a PAD District basis.

Supply source: May be a single completion, a single well, a single field with one or more reservoirs, several fields under a single gas-purchase contract, miscellaneous fields, a processing plant, or a field area, provided, however, that the geographic area encompassed by a single supply source may not be larger than the state in which the reserves are reported.

Supply, petroleum: A set of categories used to account for how crude oil and petroleum products are transferred, distributed, or placed into the supply stream. The categories include field production, refinery production, and imports. Net receipts are also included on a Petroleum Administration for Defense (PAD) district basis to account for shipments of crude oil and petroleum products across districts.

Sweet crude: Crude oil with low sulfur content, which is less corrosive, burns cleaner, and requires less processing to yield valuable products.

Syncline: A downfold in stratified rock that looks like an upright bowl. Unfavorable to the accumulation of oil and gas.

Synthetic crude oil (syncrude): A crude oil derived from processing carbonaceous material such as shale oil or refined oil in coal conversion processes.

Synthetic natural gas (SNG): Also referred to as substitute natural gas. A manufactured product resulting from the conversion or reforming of hydrocarbons, chemically similar in most respects to natural gas, that may easily be used as a substitute.

T

T: Trillion.

t: Tenth.

Tailgate: The outlet of a natural gas processing plant where dry residue gas is delivered or redelivered for sale or transportation.

Tangible development costs: Costs incurred during the development stage for access, mineral-handling, and support facilities having a physical nature. In mining, such costs would include tracks, lighting equipment, ventilation equipment, other equipment installed in the mine to facilitate the extraction of minerals, and supporting facilities for housing and care of work forces. In the oil and gas industry, tangible development costs would include well equipment (such as casing, tubing, pumping equipment, and well heads), as well as field storage tanks and gathering systems.

Tar sands: Naturally occurring bitumen-impregnated sands that yield mixtures of liquid hydrocarbon and that require further processing other than mechanical blending before becoming finished petroleum products.

Tariff: A published volume of rate schedules and general terms and conditions under which a product or service will be supplied.

TCF: Trillion cubic feet.

Tennessee Valley Authority (TVA): A federal agency established in 1933 to develop the Tennessee River Valley region of the southeastern US.

Terawatthour: One trillion watt hours.

Tertiary recovery: The recovery of oil that involves complex and very expensive methods such as the injection of steam, chemicals, gases, or heat, as compared to primary recovery, which involves depleting a naturally flowing reservoir, or secondary recovery, which usually involves repressuring or waterflooding.

th: Thousandth.

Therm: One hundred thousand (100,000) Btu.

Thermal: A term used to identify a type of electric generating station, capacity, capability, or output in which the source of energy for the prime mover is heat.

Thermal conversion factor: A factor for converting data between physical units of measure (such as barrels, cubic feet, or short tons) and thermal units of measure (such as British thermal units, calories, or joules); or for converting data between different thermal units of measure.

Thermal cracking: A refining process in which heat and pressure are used to break down, rearrange, or combine hydrocarbon molecules. Thermal-cracking includes gas oil, visbreaking, fluid coking, delayed coking, and other thermal cracking processes (e.g., flexicoking).

Thermal efficiency: A measure of the efficiency of converting a fuel to energy and useful work; useful work and energy output divided by higher heating value of input fuel times 100 (for percent).

Thermal energy storage: The storage of heat energy during utility off-peak times at night, for use during the next day without incurring daytime peak electric rates.

Thermal limit: The maximum amount of power a transmission line can carry without suffering heat-related deterioration of line equipment, particularly conductors.

Thermal rating (electric): The maximum amount of electrical current that a transmission line or electrical facility can conduct over a specified time period before it sustains permanent damage by overheating or before it sags to the point that it violates public safety requirements.

Thermal resistance (R-value): This designates the resistance of a material to heat conduction. The greater the R-value, the larger the number.

Thermal storage: Storage of heat or heat sinks (coldness) for later heating or cooling. Examples are the storage of solar energy for night heating, the storage of summer heat for winter use, the storage of winter ice for space cooling in the summer, and the storage of electrically-generated heat or coolness when electricity is less expensive, to be released in order to avoid using electricity when the rates are higher. There are four basic types of thermal storage systems: ice storage; water storage; storage in rock, soil, or other types of solid thermal mass; and storage in other materials, such as glycol (antifreeze).

Thermodynamics: A study of the transformation of energy from one form to another, and its practical application.

Thermophotovoltaic cell: A device where sunlight concentrated onto an absorber heats it to a high temperature, and the thermal radiation emitted by the absorber is used as the energy source for a photovoltaic cell that is designed to maximize conversion efficiency at the wavelength of the thermal radiation.

Transmission (electric): An interconnected group of lines and associated equipment for the movement or transfer of electric energy between points of supply and points at which it is transformed for delivery to customers or is delivered to other electric systems.

Transmission line: A set of conductors, insulators, supporting structures, and associated equipment used to move large quantities of power at high voltage, usually over long distances between a generating or receiving point and major substations or delivery points.

Transmission service provider (electric): The entity that administers the transmission tariff and provides transmission service to transmission customers under applicable transmission service agreements.

Transmitting utility: A regulated entity that owns and may construct and maintain wires used to transmit wholesale power. It may or may not handle the power dispatch and coordination functions. It is regulated to provide non-discriminatory connections, comparable service, and cost recovery.

Transport: Movement of natural, synthetic, and supplemental gas between points beyond the immediate vicinity of the field or plant from which produced except for 1) movements through well or field lines to a central point for delivery to a pipeline or processing plant within the same state or 2) movements from a city gate point of receipt to consumers through distribution mains.

Trunk line: A main pipeline.

Turbine: A machine for generating rotary mechanical power from the energy of a stream of fluid (such as water, steam, or hot gas). Turbines convert the kinetic energy of fluids to mechanical energy through the principles of impulse and reaction, or a mixture of the two.

U

Unbundling: Separating vertically integrated monopoly functions into their component parts for the purpose of separate service offerings.

Unconventional oil and natural gas production: An umbrella term for oil and natural gas that is produced by means that do not meet the criteria for conventional production.

Underground gas storage: The use of sub-surface facilities for storing gas that has been transferred from its original location. The facilities are usually hollowed-out salt domes, geological reservoirs (depleted oil or gas fields) or water-bearing sands topped by an impermeable cap rock (aquifer).

Underground gas storage reservoir capacity: Interstate company reservoir capacities are those certificated by the Federal Energy Regulatory Commission. Independent producer and intrastate company reservoir capacities are reported as developed capacity.

Underground storage: The storage of natural gas in underground reservoirs at a different location from which it was produced.

Underground storage injections: Gas from extraneous sources put into underground storage reservoirs.

Underground storage withdrawals: Gas removed from underground storage reservoirs.

Undiscovered recoverable reserves (crude oil and natural gas): Those economic resources of crude oil and natural gas, yet undiscovered, that are estimated to exist in favorable geologic settings.

Upstream: Activities concerned with finding petroleum and producing it, compared to downstream, which are all the operations that take place after producing.

Uranium (U): A heavy, naturally radioactive, metallic element (atomic number 92). Its two principally occurring isotopes are uranium-235 and uranium-238. Uranium-235 is indispensable to the nuclear industry because it is the only isotope existing in nature, to any appreciable extent, that is fissionable by thermal neutrons. Uranium-238 is also important because it absorbs neutrons to produce a radioactive isotope that subsequently decays to the isotope plutonium-239, which also is fissionable by thermal neutrons.

Uranium ore: Rock containing uranium mineralization in concentrations that can be mined economically, typically one to four pounds of U3O8 per ton or 0.05 percent to 0.2 percent U3O8.

Uranium oxide: Uranium concentrate or yellowcake. Abbreviated as U3O8.

Uranium reserves: Estimated quantities of uranium in known mineral deposits of such size, grade, and configuration that the uranium could be recovered at or below a specified production cost with currently proven mining and processing technology and under current law and regulations. Reserves are based on direct radiometric and chemical measurements of drill holes and other types of sampling of the deposits. Mineral grades and thickness, spatial relationships, depths below the surface, mining and reclamation methods, distances to milling facilities, and amenability of ores to processing are considered in the evaluation. The amount of uranium in ore that could be exploited within the chosen forward-cost levels are estimated in accordance with conventional engineering practices.

V

Volt (V): The volt is the International System of Units (SI) measure of electric potential or electromotive force. A potential of one volt appears across a resistance of one ohm when a current of one ampere flows through that resistance. Reduced to SI base units, $1\ V = 1 kg \times m^2 \times s^{-3} \times A^{-1}$ (kilogram meter squared per second cubed per ampere).

Vacuum distillation: Distillation under reduced pressure (less the atmospheric) which lowers the boiling temperature of the liquid being distilled. This technique with its relatively low temperatures prevents cracking or decomposition of the charge stock.

Vehicle fuel consumption: Vehicle fuel consumption is computed as the vehicle miles traveled divided by the fuel efficiency reported in miles per gallon (MPG). Vehicle fuel consumption is derived from the actual vehicle mileage collected and the assigned MPGs obtained from EPA certification files adjusted for on-road driving. The quantity of fuel used by vehicles.

Vehicle fuel efficiencies: Fuel efficiency is a form of thermal efficiency, meaning the efficiency of a process that converts chemical potential energy contained in a carrier fuel into kinetic energy or work.

Viscosity: A fluid's resistance to flowing.

W

Watt (W): The unit of electrical power equal to one ampere under a pressure of one volt. A Watt is equal to 1/746 horse power.

WACOG: Weighted average cost of gas.

Water reservoir: A large inland body of water collected and stored above ground in a natural or artificial formation.

Water source heat pump: A type of (geothermal) heat pump that uses well (ground) or surface water as a heat source. Water has a more stable seasonal temperature than air, making for a more efficient heat source.

Water turbine: A turbine that uses water pressure to rotate its blades; the primary types are the Pelton wheel, for high heads (pressure); the Francis turbine, for low to medium heads; and the Kaplan for a wide range of heads. Primarily used to power an electric generator.

Watthour (Wh): The electrical energy unit of measure equal to one watt of power supplied to or taken from an electric circuit steadily for one hour.

Wattmeter: A device for measuring power consumption.

Wax: A solid or semi-solid material consisting of a mixture of hydrocarbons obtained or derived from petroleum fractions, or through a Fischer-Tropsch type process, in which the straight-chained paraffin series predominates. This includes all marketable wax, whether crude or refined, with a congealing point (ASTM D

938) between 100°F and 200°F and a maximum oil content (ASTM D 3235) of 50 weight percent.

Well: A hole drilled in the earth for the purpose of 1) finding or producing crude oil or natural gas, or 2) producing services related to the production of crude or natural gas.

Wellhead: The point at which the crude (or natural gas) exits the ground. Following historical precedent, the volume and price for crude oil production are labeled as "wellhead," even though the cost and volume are now generally measured at the lease boundary. In the context of domestic crude price data, the term "wellhead" is the generic term used to reference the production site or lease property.

Wellhead price: The value at the mouth of the well. In general, the wellhead price is considered to be the sales price obtainable from a third party in an arm's length transaction. Posted prices, requested prices, or prices as defined by lease agreements, contracts, or tax regulations should be used where applicable.

West Texas Intermediate (WTI—Cushing): A crude stream produced in Texas and southern Oklahoma, which serves as a reference or "marker" for pricing a number of other crude streams and is traded in the domestic spot market at Cushing, Oklahoma.

Wet natural gas: A mixture of hydrocarbon compounds and small quantities of various non-hydrocarbons existing in the gaseous phase or in solution with crude oil in porous rock formations at reservoir conditions. The principal hydrocarbons normally contained in the mixture are methane, ethane, propane, butane, and pentane. Typical non-hydrocarbon gases that may be present in reservoir natural gas are water vapor, carbon dioxide, hydrogen sulfide, nitrogen, and trace amounts of helium. Under reservoir conditions, natural gas and its associated liquefiable portions occur either in a single gaseous phase in the reservoir or in solution with crude oil and are not distinguishable at the time as separate substances. **Note:** The Securities and Exchange

Commission and the Financial Accounting Standards Board refer to this product as natural gas.

Wind energy: Kinetic energy present in wind motion that can be converted to mechanical energy for driving pumps, mills, and electric power generators.

Wind energy conversion system (WECS) or device: An apparatus for converting the energy available in the wind to mechanical energy that can be used to power machinery (grain mills, water pumps) and to operate an electrical generator.

Wind farm or wind power plant: A group of wind turbines interconnected to a common utility system through a system of transformers, distribution lines, and (usually) one substation. Operation, control, and maintenance functions are often centralized through a network of computerized monitoring systems, supplemented by visual inspection. This is a term commonly used in the United States. In Europe, it is called a generating station.

Wind turbine: Wind energy conversion device that produces electricity; typically three blades rotating about a horizontal axis and positioned upwind of the supporting tower.

Wood conversion to Btu: Converting cords of wood into a Btu equivalent is an imprecise procedure. The number of cords each household reports having burned is inexact, even with the more precise drawings provided, because the estimate requires the respondent to add up the use of wood over a twelve-month period during which wood may have been added to the supply as well as removed. Besides errors of memory inherent in this task, the estimates are subject to problems in definition and perception of what a cord is. The nominal cord as delivered to a suburban residential buyer may differ from the dimensions of the standard cord. This difference is possible because wood is most often cut in lengths that are longer than what makes a third of a cord (sixteen inches) and shorter than what makes a half cord (twenty-four inches). In other cases, wood is bought or cut in unusual units (for example, pickup-truck load or trunk load). Finally, volume estimates are difficult to make when the wood is left in a pile instead of being stacked. Other factors that make it difficult to estimate the Btu value of the wood burned is that the amount of empty space between the stacked logs may vary from 12 to 40 percent of the volume. Moisture content may vary from 20 percent in dried wood to 50 percent in green wood. (Moisture reduces the useful Btu output because energy is used in driving off the moisture). Finally, some tree species contain twice the Btu content of species with the lowest Btu value. Generally, hard woods have greater Btu value than soft woods. Wood is converted to Btu at the rate of 20 million Btu per cord, which is a rough average that takes all these factors into account.

Working interest: An interest in a mineral property that entitles the owner of that interest to all of the share of the mineral production from the property, usually subject to a royalty. A working interest permits the owner to explore, develop, and operate the property. The working interest owner bears the costs of exploration, development, and operation of the property and, in return, is entitled to a share of the mineral production from the property or to a share of the proceeds there from. It may be assigned to another party in whole or in part, or it may be divided into other special property interests.

- Gross working interest: The reporting company's working interest plus the proportionate share of any basic royalty interest or overriding royalty interest related to the working interest.
- Net working interest: The reporting company's working interest does not include any basic royalty or overriding royalty interests.

XYZ

Xylene (C$_6$H$_4$(CH$_3$)$_2$): Colorless liquid of the aromatic group of hydrocarbons made the catalytic reforming of certain naphthenic petroleum fractions. Used as high-octane motor and aviation gasoline blending agents, solvents, chemical intermediates. Isomers are metaxylene, orthoxylene, paraxylene.

Yellowcake: A natural uranium concentrate that takes its name from its color and texture. Yellowcake typically contains 70 to 90 percent U3O8 (uranium oxide) by weight. It is used as feedstock for uranium fuel enrichment and fuel pellet fabrication.

References for Forms and Glossary:

www.eia.gov

www.energysavers.gov

www.energy.gov

Calculator that can be used to calculate/configure information:
www.ConsumerReports.org/cro/resources/images/video/
wattage_calculator/wattage_calculator.html

About the Author

Photo by Mandy Stansberry Photography

Mark A. Stansberry is an international businessman, energy leader, and humanitarian from Edmond, Oklahoma. He is the founder and chairman of The GTD Group, author of *The Braking Point: America's Energy Dreams and Global Economic Realities*, host of *The Weekly Roundtable* radio show on KFAQ 1170 AM in Tulsa, and chairman of People to People International, a Kansas City-based nonprofit organization that promotes world peace through cultural education and understanding.

Stansberry currently serves on the Board of Directors for PostRock Energy Corp. (PSTR, NASDAQ-Global) and is an ex-officio Board member and served from 2003 to 2009 as president of The Energy Advocates, a Washington, DC- and Tulsa-based nonprofit public education organization with former Oklahoma Governor Frank Keating serving as honorary chairman. He served from 2003 to 2010 as chairman of the State Chamber of Oklahoma Energy Council and founded the International Energy Policy Conference, now in its twentieth year. For more information, visit www.EnergyPolicyConference.com.

With more than thirty-five years of direct experience in the energy industry, Stansberry has become a respected industry expert and media commentator on energy issues. He has testified before the US Senate Energy and Natural Resources Committee, appeared on national TV networks including CNN, and has been quoted in newspapers and magazines such as the *Wall Street Journal Market Watch*. Stansberry is a frequent guest on radio shows, publishes op-eds, and presents speeches throughout the United States and globally.

In 1991 Stansberry coauthored an energy industry handbook, *The Acquisition Process and Due Diligence: Minimize Risk/Maximize Return!* In 2001 he cofounded an independent film production company with Academy Award-winning producer Gray Frederickson (*The Godfather: Part II*). Their most recent project is *The GET (Grand Energy Transition),* a documentary film about the future of energy, based on the book by Oklahoma energy leader Robert A. Hefner III. *The GET* is scheduled for release in 2012.